Top 300 Drugs

Practice Question Workbook

Renee Bonsell, PharmD, RPh

CONTENTS

DRUGS A – B

QUESTIONS

Acyclovir

1. Which of the following is a brand name for acyclovir?

a. Xenical
b. Denavir
c. Zovirax
d. Midrin

2. Acyclovir belongs to which of the following pharmacologic classes?

a. Antibiotic
b. Antiprotozoal
c. Antidiarrheal
d. Antiviral

3. Acyclovir is available in all but which of the following dosage forms?

a. Nasal spray
b. Topical cream
c. Oral tablet
d. Oral capsule

Adalimumab

4. Which of the following is the brand name for adalimumab?

a. Zemplar
b. Humira
c. Feldene
d. Prolia

5. Adalimumab belongs to which of the following pharmacologic classes?

a. Alpha-agonist
b. Corticosteroid
c. Benzodiazepine
d. Monoclonal antibody

6. Adalimumab is available in which of the following dosage forms?

a. Subcutaneous injection
b. Transdermal patch
c. Topical ointment
d. Inhalation solution

7. Adalimumab has a black box warning regarding the risk of which of the following?

a. Osteonecrosis
b. Serious infections
c. Arrhythmias
d. Pancreatitis

Albuterol

8. All but which of the following is a brand name for albuterol?

a. ProAir HFA
b. Ventolin HFA
c. Proventil HFA
d. Dulera HFA

9. Albuterol belongs to which of the following pharmacologic classes?

a. Antihistamine
b. Mast cell stabilizer
c. Beta$_2$-agonist
d. Vasodilator

10. Albuterol is available in which of the following dosage forms?

a. Oral capsule
b. Inhalation solution
c. Intravenous solution
d. Nasal spray

Albuterol-ipratropium

11. Which of the following is a brand name for albuterol-ipratropium?

a. DuoNeb
b. Nardil
c. Daliresp
d. Toradol

12. Albuterol-ipratropium is indicated for the treatment of which of the following conditions?

a. Bronchitis
b. COPD
c. Pneumonia
d. Tuberculosis

13. Albuterol-ipratropium is available in which of the following dosage forms?

a. Oral solution
b. Oral tablet
c. Nebulizer solution
d. Intravenous solution

Alendronate

14. Which of the following is a brand name for alendronate?

a. Fosamax
b. Uroxatral
c. Boniva
d. Enbrel

15. Alendronate belongs to which of the following pharmacologic classes?

a. Calcium channel blocker
b. Antacid
c. Bisphosphonate
d. SSRI

16. Alendronate is indicated for the treatment of which of the following conditions?

a. Epilepsy
b. Osteoporosis
c. Anxiety
d. Hypertension

17. Patients should remain upright after taking alendronate to prevent which of the following adverse effects?

a. Esophageal irritation
b. Headache
c. Abdominal pain
d. Muscle cramps

Allopurinol

18. Which of the following is a brand name for allopurinol?

a. Neurontin
b. Atacand
c. Librium
d. Zyloprim

19. Allopurinol is indicated for the treatment of which of the following conditions?

a. Hyperlipidemia
b. Eczema
c. Gout
d. Fungal infections

20. Allopurinol is available in which of the following oral tablet strengths?

a. 50 mg
b. 100 mg
c. 200 mg
d. 250 mg

Alprazolam

21. Which of the following is a brand name for alprazolam?

a. Xanax
b. Ativan
c. Welchol
d. Alvesco

22. Alprazolam belongs to which of the following pharmacologic classes?

a. Diuretic
b. SNRI
c. Antiemetic
d. Benzodiazepine

23. Alprazolam is available in all but which of the following dosage forms?

a. Oral tablet
b. Intravenous solution
c. Oral disintegrating tablet
d. Oral solution

Amiodarone

24. Which of the following is a brand name for amiodarone?

a. Keppra
b. Arava
c. Pacerone
d. Dalmane

25. Amiodarone belongs to which of the following pharmacologic classes?

a. Antiarrhythmic
b. Sulfonylurea
c. Immunosuppressant
d. ARB

26. Amiodarone has a black box warning regarding the risk of which of the following?

a. Thyroid tumors
b. Retinopathy
c. Anemia
d. Pulmonary toxicity

Amitriptyline

27. Which of the following is a brand name for amitriptyline?

a. Relpax
b. Elavil
c. Detrol
d. Besivance

28. Amitriptyline belongs to which of the following pharmacologic classes?

a. Tricyclic antidepressant
b. SNRI
c. Anticonvulsant
d. SSRI

29. Amitriptyline is available in which of the following dosage forms?

a. Oral capsule
b. Intramuscular injection
c. Oral tablet
d. Oral solution

Amlodipine

30. Which of the following is the brand name for amlodipine?

a. Emend
b. Aciphex
c. Halcion
d. Norvasc

31. Amlodipine belongs to which of the following pharmacologic classes?

a. Beta-blocker
b. Calcium channel blocker
c. Potassium channel blocker
d. Sodium channel blocker

32. Which of the following is the highest strength that is available for amlodipine oral tablets?

a. 5 mg
b. 10 mg
c. 15 mg
d. 20 mg

Amlodipine-benazepril

33. Which of the following is the brand name for amlodipine-benazepril?

a. Lotrel
b. Caduet
c. Azor
d. Exforge

34. Amlodipine-benazepril is indicated for the treatment of which of the following conditions?

a. Overactive bladder
b. Edema
c. Hypertension
d. Diabetes

35. Amlodipine-benazepril is available in which of the following dosage forms?

a. Oral suspension
b. Intravenous solution
c. Oral tablet
d. Oral capsule

Amoxicillin

36. Which of the following is a brand name for amoxicillin?

a. Amoxil
b. Ranexa
c. Zyvox
d. Infed

37. Amoxicillin belongs to which of the following pharmacologic classes?

a. Fluoroquinolone antibiotic
b. Cephalosporin antibiotic
c. Penicillin antibiotic
d. Macrolide antibiotic

38. Amoxicillin is available in all but which of the following dosage forms?

a. Oral capsule
b. Intramuscular solution
c. Oral tablet
d. Oral suspension

Amoxicillin-clavulanate

39. Which of the following is a brand name for amoxicillin-clavulanate?

a. Xolair
b. Moxatag
c. Trimox
d. Augmentin

40. Clavulanate is combined with amoxicillin for which of the following reasons?

a. Decrease side effects
b. Prevent allergic reactions
c. Improve palatability
d. Prevent degradation of amoxicillin

41. Which of the following administration techniques applies to amoxicillin-clavulanate?

a. Take with food.
b. Avoid antacids.
c. Take on an empty stomach.
d. Avoid alcohol.

Amphetamine-dextroamphetamine

42. Which of the following is a brand name for amphetamine-dextroamphetamine?

a. Risperdal
b. Natrecor
c. Adderall
d. Oracea

43. Amphetamine-dextroamphetamine belongs to which of the following pharmacologic classes?

a. Anticonvulsant
b. Antipyschotic
c. Sedative
d. CNS Stimulant

44. Amphetamine-dextroamphetamine belongs to which of the following DEA Schedules?

a. Schedule II
b. Schedule III
c. Schedule IV
d. Schedule V

Anastrozole

45. Which of the following is the brand name for anastrozole?

a. Starlix
b. Arimidex
c. Estratest
d. Geodon

46. Anastrozole belongs to which of the following pharmacologic classes?

a. Bile acid sequestrant
b. SSRI
c. Meglitinide
d. Aromatase inhibitor

47. Anastrozole is indicated for the treatment of which of the following?

a. Colon cancer
b. Lung cancer
c. Breast cancer
d. Prostate cancer

48. Anastrozole is available in which of the following dosage forms?

a. Oral tablet
b. Subcutaneous solution
c. Intramuscular suspension
d. Oral capsule

Apixaban

49. Which of the following is the brand name for apixaban?

a. Daypro
b. Campral
c. Accupril
d. Eliquis

50. Apixaban belongs to which of the following pharmacologic classes?

a. Hematopoietic agent
b. Anticoagulant
c. NSAID
d. H_2 receptor antagonist

51. Apixiban is indicated for all but which of the following conditions?

a. Prevention of myocardial infarction (MI)
b. Treatment of deep vein thrombosis (DVT)
c. Treatment of pulmonary embolism (PE)
d. Prevention of stroke in nonvalvular atrial fibrillation (NVAF)

Aripiprazole

52. Which of the following is the brand name for aripiprazole?

a. Invega
b. Byetta
c. Abilify
d. Lunesta

53. Aripiprazole belongs to which of the following pharmacologic classes?

a. Hypnotic
b. Antipsychotic
c. Cytoprotective agent
d. Antimanic agent

54. Aripiprazole is available in all but which of the following dosage forms?

a. Oral tablet
b. Intramuscular injection
c. Oral solution
d. Intravenous solution

55. Aripiprazole has a black box warning regarding an increased risk of death when used in which of the following patient populations?

a. Female patients with bipolar disorder
b. Male patients with schizophrenia
c. Elderly patients with dementia
d. Female patients with depression

Aspirin-dipyridamole

56. Which of the following is the brand name for aspirin-dipyridamole?

a. Aggrenox
b. Vimpat
c. Cardura
d. Persantine

57. Aspirin-dipyridamole is available in which of the following oral capsule strengths?

a. 15 mg-50 mg
b. 15 mg-100 mg
c. 25 mg-150 mg
d. 25 mg-200 mg

58. When used for stroke prevention, aspirin-dipyridamole is dosed _____ time(s) daily.

a. one
b. two
c. three
d. four

Atenolol

59. Which of the following is the brand name for atenolol?

a. Lamisil
b. Combivir
c. Tenormin
d. Qsymia

60. Atenolol belongs to which of the following pharmacologic classes?

a. Alpha$_1$-blocker
b. Beta$_1$-blocker
c. Beta$_2$-blocker
d. Beta$_1$- and beta$_2$-blocker

61. Atenolol is indicated for the treatment of which of the following conditions?

a. Atherosclerosis
b. Transient ischemic attack
c. Heart failure
d. Angina

62. Atenolol may mask symptoms of which of the following conditions?

a. Hypoglycemia
b. Hypocalcemia
c. Hyperkalemia
d. Hypermagnesemia

Atenolol-chlorthalidone

63. Which of the following is the brand name for atenolol-chlorthalidone?

a. Accolate
b. Tenoretic
c. Sonata
d. Lupron

64. Atenolol-chlorthalidone is indicated for the treatment of which of the following conditions?

a. Myocardial infarction
b. Angina
c. Heart valve disease
d. Hypertension

65. Atenolol-chlorthalidone is available in which of the following dosage forms?

a. Intravenous solution
b. Oral capsule
c. Oral tablet
d. Oral solution

Atomoxetine

66. Which of the following is the brand name for atomoxetine?

a. Strattera
b. Depakene
c. Vaniqa
d. Latisse

67. Atomoxetine is indicated for the treatment of which of the following conditions?

a. Depression
b. ADHD
c. Diabetes
d. Hypothyroidism

68. Atomoxetine inhibits the reuptake of which of the following neurotransmitters?

a. Acetylcholine
b. Serotonin
c. Dopamine
d. Norepinephrine

Atorvastatin

69. Which of the following is the brand name for atorvastatin?

a. Lipitor
b. Kepivance
c. Skelaxin
d. Livalo

70. Atorvastatin belongs to which of the following pharmacologic classes?

a. Cholesterol absorption inhibitor
b. Bile acid sequestrant
c. HMG-CoA reductase inhibitor
d. Fibric acid derivative

71. Which of the following is the highest strength that is available for atorvastatin oral tablets?

a. 20 mg
b. 40 mg
c. 60 mg
d. 80 mg

72. The levels of atorvastatin may be increased by which of the following?

a. Grapefruit juice
b. Alcohol
c. Dairy products
d. Orange juice

Azathioprine

73. Which of the following is a brand name for azathioprine?

a. Colazal
b. Imuran
c. Nebupent
d. Sporanox

74. Azathioprine belongs to which of the following pharmacologic classes?

a. Antibiotic
b. Respiratory agent
c. Anorexiant
d. Immunosuppressant

75. Azathioprine is indicated for the treatment of which of the following conditions?

a. Graves' disease
b. Ulcerative colitis
c. Rheumatoid arthritis
d. Guillain-Barre syndrome

Azelastine

76. Which of the following is a brand name for azelastine?

a. Edarbi
b. Astepro
c. Nexplanon
d. Dymista

77. Azelastine belongs to which of the following pharmacologic classes?

a. Antidepressant
b. Anticoagulant
c. Antihistamine
d. Analgesic

78. Azelastine is available in which of the following dosage forms?

a. Nasal spray
b. Oral tablet
c. Inhalation solution
d. Nebulizer solution

Azithromycin

79. Which of the following is a brand name for azithromycin?

a. Belviq
b. Xalatan
c. Jalyn
d. Zithromax

80. Azithromycin belongs to which of the following pharmacologic classes?

a. Aminoglycoside antibiotic
b. Penicillin antibiotic
c. Macrolide antibiotic
d. Cephalosporin antibiotic

81. Azithromycin is indicated for the treatment of which of the following types of infections?

a. Community-acquired pneumonia
b. Urinary tract infection
c. Infective endocarditis
d. Meningitis

82. Which of the following is the correct dosing regimen for azithromycin that is packaged as a Z-Pak?

a. 250 mg daily for 5 days
b. 500 mg on day 1, followed by 250 mg daily on days 2 to 5
c. 500 mg daily on days 1 and 2, followed by 250 mg daily on days 3 and 4
d. 500 mg daily for 3 days

Baclofen

83. Which of the following is a brand name for baclofen?

a. Kayexalate
b. Santyl
c. Vasotec
d. Lioresal

84. Baclofen belongs to which of the following pharmacologic classes?

a. Muscle relaxant
b. Opioid analgesic
c. Antianxiety agent
d. Antihypertensive

85. Baclofen is available in which of the following oral tablet strengths?

a. 5 mg
b. 15 mg
c. 20 mg
d. 40 mg

Beclomethasone

86. Which of the following is a brand name for beclomethasone?

a. Hydrea
b. Qvar
c. Cortisporin
d. Savella

87. Beclomethasone belongs to which of the following pharmacologic classes?

a. Corticosteroid
b. Loop diuretic
c. Alpha$_1$-blocker
d. Anticholinergic

88. Beclomethasone is available in which of the following dosage forms?

a. Nebulizer solution
b. Rectal suppository
c. Inhalation solution
d. Oral tablet

Benazepril

89. Which of the following is the brand name for benazepril?

a. Vyvanse
b. Lotensin
c. Stalevo
d. Nuvigil

90. Benazepril belongs to which of the following pharmacologic classes?

a. Antihypertensive
b. Antifungal
c. Anticonvulsant
d. Inotropic agent

91. Benazepril is available in all but which of the following oral tablet strengths?

a. 10 mg
b. 20 mg
c. 40 mg
d. 80 mg

Benzonatate

92. Which of the following is a brand name for benzonatate?

a. TussiCaps
b. Famvir
c. Tessalon Perles
d. Zonegran

93. Benzonatate is indicated for the treatment of which of the following conditions?

a. Cough
b. Muscle spasms
c. Pruritis
d. Edema

94. Which of the following is the maximum daily dose for benzonatate?

a. 200 mg
b. 400 mg
c. 600 mg
d. 800 mg

95. Benzonatate may cause which of the following adverse effects?

a. Sweating
b. Drowsiness
c. Heartburn
d. Dry mouth

Benztropine

96. Which of the following is the brand name for benztropine?

a. Cogentin
b. Loprox
c. Zofran
d. Unasyn

97. Benztropine belongs to which of the following pharmacologic classes?

a. Analgesic
b. Laxative
c. Antipsychotic
d. Anticholinergic

98. Benztropine is indicated for the treatment of which of the following conditions?

a. COPD
b. Parkinson's disease
c. Dementia
d. Angina

Bimatoprost

99. Which of the following is a brand name for bimatoprost?

a. Lumigan
b. Velcade
c. AzaSite
d. Trileptal

100. Bimatoprost belongs to which of the following pharmacologic classes?

a. Antibiotic
b. PPI
c. Nasal decongestant
d. Antiglaucoma agent

101. Bimatoprost may cause all but which of the following adverse effects?

a. Iris depigmentation
b. Dry eye
c. Eyelid hyperpigmentation
d. Eyelash growth

Bisoprolol-hydrochlorothiazide

102. Which of the following is the brand name for bisoprolol-hydrochlorothiazide?

a. Lescol XL
b. Benicar HCT
c. Ziac
d. Malarone

103. Bisoprolol-hydrochlorothiazide is a combination of which of the following classes of medications?

a. Beta-blocker and diuretic
b. Calcium channel blocker and diuretic
c. ARB and diuretic
d. ACE inhibitor and diuretic

104. Bisoprolol-hydrochlorothiazide is available in which of the following dosage forms?

a. Oral solution
b. Oral capsule
c. Intravenous solution
d. Oral tablet

Brimonidine

105. Which of the following is a brand name for brimonidine?

a. Gabitril
b. TobraDex
c. Mevacor
d. Alphagan P

106. Brimonidine belongs to which of the following pharmacologic classes?

a. SSRI
b. Alpha$_2$-agonist
c. Beta-blocker
d. PPI

107. Brimonidine is indicated for the treatment of which of the following conditions?

a. Psoriasis
b. Nasal congestion
c. Glaucoma
d. BPH

Budesonide

108. Which of the following is a brand name for budesonide?

a. Pulmicort
b. Lotronex
c. Spiriva
d. Giazo

109. Budesonide belongs to which of the following pharmacologic classes?

a. Antiviral
b. Antihyperlipidemic
c. Corticosteroid
d. Erectile dysfunction agent

110. Budesonide is available in all but which of the following dosage forms?

a. Oral capsule
b. Rectal suppository
c. Inhalation suspension
d. Nasal spray

Budesonide-formoterol

111. Which of the following is the brand name for budesonide-formoterol?

a. Breo Ellipta
b. Uceris
c. Cytra-K
d. Symbicort

112. Budesonide-formoterol is indicated for the treatment of which of the following conditions?

a. COPD
b. Allergic rhinitis
c. Pneumonia
d. Chron's disease

113. Budesonide-formoterol is available in which of the following dosage forms?

a. Nasal spray
b. Inhalation aerosol
c. Intravenous solution
d. Oral capsule

Buprenorphine-naloxone

114. Which of the following is a brand name for buprenorphine-naloxone?

a. Zymaxid
b. Razadyne
c. Suboxone
d. Narcan

115. Buprenorphine-naloxone is indicated for the treatment of which of the following conditions?

a. Opioid dependence
b. Alzheimer's disease
c. Depression
d. Alcoholism

116. Buprenorphine-naloxone is available in which of the following dosage forms?

a. Oral capsule
b. Intravenous solution
c. Intramuscular suspension
d. Sublingual tablet

Bupropion

117. Which of the following is a brand name for bupropion?

a. Zyprexa
b. Otezla
c. Wellbutrin XL
d. Emend

118. Bupropion is indicated for the treatment of all but which of the following conditions?

a. Schizophrenia
b. Smoking cessation
c. Depression
d. Seasonal affective disorder

119. Bupropion is available in which of the following dosage forms?

a. Transdermal patch
b. Oral tablet
c. Oral capsule
d. Oral suspension

120. Bupropion inhibits the reuptake of which of the following neurotransmitters?

a. Serotonin
b. Dopamine
c. Serotonin and norepinephrine
d. Dopamine and norepinephrine

Buspirone

121. Which of the following is a brand name for buspirone?

a. Hytrin
b. Avalide
c. BuSpar
d. Spectazole

122. Buspirone belongs to which of the following pharmacologic classes?

a. Antibiotic
b. Chemotherapeutic agent
c. Osteoporosis agent
d. Antianxiety agent

123. Buspirone is available in all but which of the following oral tablet strengths?

a. 2.5 mg
b. 5 mg
c. 7.5 mg
d. 10 mg

ANSWER KEY

1. C
A brand name for acyclovir is Zovirax.

2. D
Acyclovir is classified as an antiviral.

3. A
Among other dosage forms, acyclovir is available as a topical cream, oral tablet, and oral capsule. Acyclovir is not available as a nasal spray.

4. B
The brand name for adalimumab is Humira.

5. D
Adalimumab is classified as a monoclonal antibody.

6. A
Adalimumab is available as a subcutaneous injection.

7. B
Adalimumab has a black box warning regarding the risk of serious infections, as well as malignancies.

8. D
ProAir HFA, Ventolin HFA, and Proventil HFA are brand names for albuterol. Dulera HFA is the brand name for mometasone-formoterol.

9. C
Albuterol is classified as a $beta_2$-agonist.

10. B
Among other dosage forms, albuterol is available as an inhalation solution.

11. A
A brand name for albuterol-ipratropium is DuoNeb.

12. B
Albuterol-ipratropium is indicated for the treatment of COPD.

13. C
Among other dosage forms, albuterol-ipratropium is available as a nebulizer solution.

14. A
A brand name for alendronate is Fosamax.

15. C
Alendronate is classified as a bisphosphonate.

16. B
Alendronate is indicated for the treatment of osteoporosis.

17. A
Patients should remain upright after taking alendronate to prevent esophageal irritation.

18. D
A brand name for allopurinol is Zyloprim.

19. C
Allopurinol is indicated for the treatment of gout.

20. B
Allopurinol is available in 100 mg oral tablets, as well as 300 mg.

21. A
A brand name for alprazolam is Xanax.

22. D
Alprazolam is classified as a benzodiazepine.

23. B
Alprazolam is available as an oral tablet, oral disintegrating tablet, and an oral solution. Alprazolam is not available as an intravenous solution.

24. C
A brand name for amiodarone is Pacerone.

25. A
Amiodarone is classified as an antiarrhythmic.

26. D
Amiodarone has a black box warning regarding the risk of pulmonary toxicity, as well as hepatic injury and worsened arrhythmia.

27. B
A brand name for amitriptyline is Elavil.

28. A
Amitriptyline is classified as a tricyclic antidepressant.

29. C
Amitriptyline is available as an oral tablet.

30. D
The brand name for amlodipine is Norvasc.

31. B
Amlodipine is classified as a calcium channel blocker.

32. B
The highest strength that is available for amlodipine oral tablets is 10 mg.

33. A
The brand name for amlodipine-benazepril is Lotrel.

34. C
Amlodipine-benazepril is indicated for the treatment of hypertension.

35. D
Amlodipine-benazepril is available as an oral capsule.

36. A
A brand name for amoxicillin is Amoxil.

37. C
Amoxicillin is classified as a penicillin antibiotic.

38. B
Amoxicillin is available as an oral capsule, oral tablet, and oral suspension. Amoxicillin is not available as an intramuscular solution.

39. D
A brand name for amoxicillin-clavulanate is Augmentin.

40. D
Clavulanate is combined with amoxicillin to prevent the degradation of amoxicillin.

41. A
Amoxicillin-clavulanate should be taken with food to increase absorption and decrease stomach upset.

42. C
A brand name for amphetamine-dextroamphetamine is Adderall.

43. D
Amphetamine-dextroamphetamine is classified as a CNS stimulant.

44. A
Amphetamine-dextroamphetamine belongs to DEA Schedule II.

45. B
The brand name for anastrozole is Arimidex.

46. D
Anastrozole is classified as an aromatase inhibitor.

47. C
Anastrozole is indicated for the treatment of breast cancer.

48. A
Anastrozole is available as an oral tablet.

49. D
The brand name for apixaban is Eliquis.

50. B
Apixaban is classified as an anticoagulant.

51. A
Among other conditions, apixiban is indicated for the treatment of deep vein thrombosis (DVT), the treatment of pulmonary embolism (PE), and the prevention of stroke in non-valvular atrial fibrillation (NVAF). Apixiban is not indicated for the prevention of myo-cardial infarction (MI).

52. C
The brand name for aripiprazole is Abilify.

53. B
Aripiprazole is classified as an antipsychotic.

54. D
Among other dosage forms, aripiprazole is available as an oral tablet, intramuscular in-jection, and an oral solution. Aripiprazole is not available as an intravenous solution.

55. C
Aripiprazole has a black box warning regarding an increased risk of death in elderly pa-tients with dementia-related psychosis.

56. A
The brand name for aspirin-dipyridamole is Aggrenox.

57. D
Aspirin-dipyridamole is available in 25 mg-200mg oral capsules.

58. B
When used for stroke prevention, aspirin-dipyridamole is dosed two times daily.

59. C
The brand name for atenolol is Tenormin.

60. B
Atenolol is classified as a beta$_1$-blocker.

61. D
Atenolol is indicated for the treatment of angina.

62. A
Atenolol may mask symptoms of hypoglycemia.

63. B
The brand name for atenolol-chlorthalidone is Tenoretic.

64. D
Atenolol-chlorthalidone is indicated for the treatment of hypertension.

65. C
Atenolol-chlorthalidone is available as an oral tablet.

66. A
The brand name for atomoxetine is Strattera.

67. B
Atomoxetine is indicated for the treatment of ADHD.

68. D
Atomoxetine inhibits the reuptake of norepinephrine.

69. A
The brand name for atorvastatin is Lipitor.

70. C
Atorvastatin is classified as an HMG-CoA reductase inhibitor.

71. D
The highest strength that is available for atorvastatin oral tablets is 80 mg.

72. A
The levels of atorvastatin may be increased by grapefruit juice.

73. B
A brand name for azathioprine is Imuran.

74. D
Azathioprine is classified as an immunosuppressant.

75. C
Among other indications, azathioprine is indicated for the treatment of rheumatoid arthritis.

76. B
A brand name for azelastine is Astepro.

77. C
Azelastine is classified as an antihistamine.

78. A
Azelastine is available as a nasal spray, as well as an ophthalmic solution.

79. D
A brand name for azithromycin is Zithromax.

80. C
Azithromycin is classified as a macrolide antibiotic.

81. A
Among other types of infections, azithromycin is indicted for the treatment of community-acquired pneumonia.

82. B
The correct dosing regimen for azithromycin that is packaged as a Z-Pak is 500 mg on day 1, followed by 250 mg daily on days 2 to 5.

83. D
A brand name for baclofen is Lioresal.

84. A
Baclofen is classified as a muscle relaxant.

85. C
Baclofen is available in 20 mg oral tablets, as well as 10 mg.

86. B
A brand name for beclomethasone is Qvar.

87. A
Beclomethasone is classified as a corticosteroid.

88. C
Beclomethasone is available as an inhalation solution, as well as a nasal spray.

89. B
The brand name for benazepril is Lotensin.

90. A
Benazepril is classified as an antihypertensive.

91. D
Benazepril is available in 5 mg, 10 mg, 20 mg, and 40 mg oral tablets. Benazepril is not available in 80 mg oral tablets.

92. C
A brand name for benzonatate is Tessalon Perles.

93. A
Benzonatate is indicated for the treatment of cough.

94. C
The maximum daily dose for benzonatate is 600 mg.

95. B
Among other adverse effects, benzonatate may cause drowsiness.

96. A
The brand name for benztropine is Cogentin.

97. D
Benztropine is classified as an anticholinergic.

98. B
Benztropine is indicated for the treatment of Parkinson's disease.

99. A
A brand name for bimatoprost is Lumigan.

100. D
Bimatoprost is classified as an antiglaucoma agent.

101. A
Among other adverse effects, bimatoprost may cause iris hyperpigmentation, dry eye, eyelid hyperpigmentation, and eyelash growth.

102. C
The brand name for bisoprolol-hydrochlorothiazide is Ziac.

103. A
Bisoprolol-hydrochlorothiazide is a combination of a beta-blocker and diuretic.

104. D
Bisoprolol-hydrochlorothiazide is available as an oral tablet.

105. D
A brand name for brimonidine is Alphagan P.

106. B
Brimonidine is classified as an alpha$_2$-agonist.

107. C
Brimonidine is indicated for the treatment of glaucoma.

108. A
A brand name for budesonide is Pulmicort.

109. C
Budesonide is classified as a corticosteroid.

110. B
Among other dosage forms, budesonide is available as an oral capsule, inhalation suspension, and nasal spray. Budesonide is not available as a rectal suppository.

111. D
The brand name for budesonide-formoterol is Symbicort.

112. A
Budesonide-formoterol is indicated for the treatment of COPD, as well as asthma.

113. B
Budesonide-formoterol is available as an inhalation aerosol.

114. C
A brand name for buprenorphine-naloxone is Suboxone.

115. A
Buprenorphine-naloxone is indicated for the treatment of opioid dependence.

116. D
Among other dosage forms, buprenorphine-naloxone is available as a sublingual tablet.

117. C
A brand name for bupropion is Wellbutrin XL.

118. A
Bupropion is indicated for smoking cessation and the treatment of depression and seasonal affective disorder. Bupropion is not indicated for the treatment of schizophrenia.

119. B
Bupropion is available as an oral tablet.

120. D
Bupropion inhibits the reuptake of dopamine and norepinephrine.

121. C
A brand name for buspirone is BuSpar.

122. D
Buspirone is classified as an antianxiety agent.

123. A
Buspirone is available in 5 mg, 7.5 mg, and 10 mg oral tablets, and also 15 mg and 30 mg. Buspirone is not available in 2.5 mg oral tablets.

DRUGS C – D

QUESTIONS

Calcitriol

1. Which of the following is a brand name for calcitriol?

a. Epzicom
b. Rocaltrol
c. Feldene
d. Asacol

2. Calcitriol belongs to which of the following pharmacologic classes?

a. Anticoagulant
b. NSAID
c. Antacid
d. Vitamin D analog

3. Calcitriol is indicated for the treatment of which of the following conditions?

a. Hypocalcemia
b. GERD
c. Hyperkalemia
d. Vertigo

Carbamazepine

4. Which of the following is a brand name for carbamazepine?

a. Prometrium
b. Clinpro
c. Tegretol
d. Rapamune

5. Carbamazepine belongs to which of the following pharmacologic classes?

a. Antiarrhythmic
b. Antidiabetic
c. Gastric antisecretory
d. Anticonvulsant

6. Carbamazepine has a black box warning regarding the risk of all but which of the following?

a. Pulmonary toxicity
b. Aplastic anemia
c. Agranulocytosis
d. Dermatologic reactions

Carbidopa-levodopa

7. Which of the following is a brand name for carbidopa-levodopa?

a. Travatan Z
b. Climara
c. Evoxac
d. Sinemet

8. Carbidopa-levodopa belongs to which of the following pharmacologic classes?

a. Antidepressant
b. Antipsychotic
c. Antiparkinson agent
d. Antihyperlipidemic

9. The absorption of carbidopa-levodopa can be decreased by which of the following?

a. Iron
b. Potassium
c. Calcium
d. Magnesium

Carisoprodol

10. Which of the following is a brand name for carisoprodol?

a. Vistaril
b. Soma
c. Aromasin
d. Lorzone

11. Carisoprodol belongs to which of the following pharmacologic classes?

a. Antibiotic
b. Analgesic
c. Skeletal muscle relaxant
d. Antihypertensive

12. Carisoprodol is available in which of the following dosage forms?

a. Oral tablet
b. Oral solution
c. Oral capsule
d. Transdermal patch

Carvedilol

13. Which of the following is the brand name for carvedilol?

a. Sotret
b. Exelon
c. Zortress
d. Coreg

14. Carvedilol belongs to which of the following pharmacologic classes?

a. Immunosuppressant
b. Antihypertensive
c. Antiviral
d. Stimulant

15. Carvedilol blocks which of the following receptors?

a. $Alpha_1$
b. $Alpha_1$ and $beta_1$
c. $Beta_1$ and $beta_2$
d. $Alpha_1$, $beta_1$, and $beta_2$

16. Which of the following administration techniques applies to carvedilol?

a. Take with food.
b. Take with plain water.
c. Take on an empty stomach.
d. Separate from vitamins and minerals.

Cefdinir

17. Which of the following is the brand name for cefdinir?

a. Halog
b. Omnicef
c. Dalmane
d. Pradaxa

18. Cefdinir belongs to which of the following pharmacologic classes?

a. Macrolide antibiotic
b. Sulfonamide antibiotic
c. Tetracycline antibiotic
d. Cephalosporin antibiotic

19. Cefdinir is available in which of the following dosage forms?

a. Oral tablet
b. Intravenous solution
c. Oral capsule
d. Intramuscular suspension

Cefuroxime

20. Which of the following is the brand name for cefuroxime?

a. Ceftin
b. Diprolene
c. Flagyl
d. Emla

21. Cefuroxime belongs to which of the following pharmacologic classes?

a. Antidiarrheal
b. Antianginal agent
c. Antihistamine
d. Antibiotic

22. Cefuroxime is available in which of the following oral tablet strengths?

a. 50 mg
b. 100 mg
c. 250 mg
d. 300 mg

Celecoxib

23. Which of the following is the brand name for celecoxib?

a. Celebrex
b. Lamictal
c. CellCept
d. Horizant

24. Celecoxib belongs to which of the following pharmacologic classes?

a. Antigout agent
b. NSAID
c. Beta-blocker
d. Antiplatelet agent

25. Celecoxib is available in which of the following dosage forms?

a. Oral capsule
b. Topical gel
c. Oral solution
d. Oral tablet

26. Celecoxib has a black box warning regarding the risk of which of the following?

a. Heart failure
b. Myelosuppression
c. Ototoxicity
d. Myocardial infarction

Cephalexin

27. Which of the following is a brand name for cephalexin?

a. Zosyn
b. Keflex
c. Luxiq
d. Azilect

28. Cephalexin belongs to which of the following pharmacologic classes?

a. Antihypertensive
b. GI antisecretory
c. Antibiotic
d. Corticosteroid

29. Cephalexin is available in all but which of the following oral capsule strengths?

a. 250 mg
b. 500 mg
c. 750 mg
d. 1,000 mg

Chlorhexidine

30. Which of the following is a brand name for chlorhexidine?

a. Peridex
b. Nizoral
c. Daypro
d. Zestril

31. Chlorhexidine belongs to which of the following pharmacologic classes?

a. Sedative
b. Antibiotic
c. Antidepressant
d. Antifungal

32. Which of the following is the most appropriate dosing for chlorhexidine when used as an oral rinse for the prevention of gingivitis?

a. Swish for 15 seconds with 15 mL twice daily
b. Swish for 30 seconds with 15 mL twice daily
c. Swish for 30 seconds with 15 mL three times daily
d. Swish for 60 seconds with 15 mL once daily

33. Chlorhexidine may cause which of the following adverse effects when used as an oral rinse?

a. Halitosis
b. Numbness
c. Dry mouth
d. Tooth discoloration

Chlorthalidone

34. Which of the following is the brand name for chlorthalidone?

a. Dilantin
b. Sandostatin
c. Thalitone
d. Vascepa

35. Chlorthalidone belongs to which of the following pharmacologic classes?

a. Thiazide-related diuretic
b. Loop diuretic
c. Potassium-sparing diuretic
d. Carbonic anhydrase inhibitor

36. Chlorthalidone is available in which of the following dosage forms?

a. Intravenous solution
b. Oral capsule
c. Subcutaneous solution
d. Oral tablet

Cholecalciferol

37. Which of the following is a brand name for cholecalciferol?

a. Delta D3
b. Opitvar
c. Poly-Vi-Sol
d. Doral

38. Cholecalciferol is available in all but which of the following dosage forms?

a. Oral capsule
b. Subcutaneous solution
c. Oral liquid
d. Oral tablet

39. How often is cholecalciferol 50,000 units typically dosed for the treatment of vitamin D deficiency?

a. Once daily
b. Once a week
c. Twice a month
d. Once a month

Ciprofloxacin

40. Which of the following is a brand name for ciprofloxacin?

a. Medrol
b. Cordran
c. Trulicity
d. Cipro

41. Ciprofloxacin belongs to which of the following pharmacologic classes?

a. Macrolide antibiotic
b. Cephalosporin antibiotic
c. Fluoroquinolone antibiotic
d. Penicillin antibiotic

42. Ciprofloxacin is available in all but which of the following dosage forms?

a. Intramuscular suspension
b. Oral tablet
c. Otic solution
d. Ophthalmic solution

43. Ciprofloxacin has a black box warning regarding the risk of which of the following?

a. Nephrotoxicity
b. *C. difficile*
c. Hypoglycemia
d. Tendon rupture

Ciprofloxacin-dexamethasone

44. Which of the following is the brand name for ciprofloxacin-dexamethasone?

a. Duexis
b. Ciprodex
c. Alli
d. Bystolic

45. Ciprofloxacin-dexamethasone is indicated for the treatment of which of the following conditions?

a. Bacterial conjunctivitis
b. Otitis externa
c. Allergic conjunctivitis
d. Inner ear infection

46. Ciprofloxacin-dexamethasone is available in which of the following dosage forms?

a. Ophthalmic solution
b. Oral tablet
c. Otic suspension
d. Oral suspension

Citalopram

47. Which of the following is the brand name for citalopram?

a. Plendil
b. Niferex
c. Kerydin
d. Celexa

48. Citalopram belongs to which of the following pharmacologic classes?

a. Antihypertensive
b. Antidepressant
c. Antianxiety agent
d. Corticosteroid

49. Citalopram may cause which of the following adverse effects?

a. QT prolongation
b. Gastric ulcers
c. Disulfiram-like reaction
d. Constipation

50. Which of the following is the highest strength available for citalopram oral tablets?

a. 10 mg
b. 20 mg
c. 40 mg
d. 80 mg

Clarithromycin

51. Which of the following is the brand name for clarithromycin?

a. Effient
b. Biaxin
c. Precose
d. Creon

52. Clarithromycin belongs to which of the following pharmacologic classes?

a. Penicillin antibiotic
b. Carbapenem antibiotic
c. Tetracycline antibiotic
d. Macrolide antibiotic

53. Clarithromycin is available in which of the following dosage forms?

a. Oral capsule
b. Intravenous solution
c. Oral suspension
d. Intramuscular suspension

Clindamycin

54. Which of the following is a brand name for clindamycin?

a. Cleocin
b. Lotemax
c. Ultresa
d. Gleevac

55. Clindamycin belongs to which of the following pharmacologic classes?

a. Antiplatelet agent
b. ARB
c. Bisphosphonate
d. Antibiotic

56. Clindamycin is available in all but which of the following dosage forms?

a. Topical lotion
b. Oral tablet
c. Intravenous solution
d. Topical gel

57. Clindamycin has a black box warning regarding the risk of which of the following?

a. Neurotoxicity
b. Rhabomyolysis
c. *Clostridium difficile*-associated diarrhea
d. Serotonin syndrome

Clobetasol

58. Which of the following is a brand name for clobetasol?

a. Temovate
b. Jardiance
c. Fanapt
d. Bactroban

59. Clobetasol belongs to which of the following pharmacologic classes?

a. Antifungal
b. Expectorant
c. Thrombolytic
d. Corticosteroid

60. Clobetasol is available in which of the following dosage forms?

a. Oral suspension
b. Topical cream
c. Rectal suppository
d. Topical oil

Clonazepam

61. Which of the following is the brand name for clonazepam?

a. Isuprel
b. Clozaril
c. Klonopin
d. Amaryl

62. Clonazepam belongs to which of the following pharmacologic classes?

a. Benzodiazepine
b. DPP-4 inhibitor
c. Statin
d. Anticholinergic

63. Clonazepam belongs to which of the following DEA Schedules?

a. Schedule II
b. Schedule III
c. Schedule IV
d. Schedule V

Clonidine

64. Which of the following is a brand name for clonidine?

a. Pamelor
b. Isentress
c. Remicade
d. Catapres

65. Clonidine belongs to which of the following pharmacologic classes?

a. Alpha$_2$-agonist
b. Antipsychotic
c. Bronchodilator
d. Beta-blocker

66. Clonidine is indicated for the treatment of which of the following conditions?

a. Erectile dysfunction
b. Hypertension
c. Obsessive compulsive disorder
d. Epilepsy

Clopidogrel

67. Which of the following is the brand name for clopidogrel?

a. Vytorin
b. Benicar
c. Olux
d. Plavix

68. Clopidogrel belongs to which of the following pharmacologic classes?

a. Anticoagulant
b. GI stimulant
c. Antiplatelet agent
d. Antihypertensive

69. Clopidogrel is available in which of the following oral tablet strengths?

a. 25 mg
b. 50 mg
c. 75 mg
d. 150 mg

70. The effectiveness of clopidogrel will be diminished in patients that have reduced function of which of the following enzymes?

a. CYP2C19
b. CYP3A4
c. CYP2D6
d. CYP2E1

Clotrimazole-betamethasone

71. Which of the following is the brand name for clotrimazole-betamethasone?

a. Terazol
b. DesOwen
c. Osphena
d. Lotrisone

72. Clotrimazole-betamethasone is a combination of which of the following classes of medications?

a. Antiviral and corticosteroid
b. Antifungal and corticosteroid
c. Antibiotic and antifungal
d. Antibiotic and corticosteroid

73. Clotrimazole-betamethasone is available in which of the following dosage forms?

a. Topical spray
b. Oral tablet
c. Topical cream
d. Shampoo

Colchicine

74. Which of the following is a brand name for colchicine?

a. Colcrys
b. Ketek
c. Trilipix
d. Requip

75. Colchicine belongs to which of the following pharmacologic classes?

a. NSAID
b. Antigout agent
c. Anticonvulsant
d. Antidepressant

76. Colchicine is available in which of the following dosage forms?

a. Intravenous solution
b. Oral solution
c. Intramuscular solution
d. Oral tablet

77. Colchicine may cause which of the following adverse effects?

a. Hepatotoxcity
b. Arthralgia
c. Diarrhea
d. Angioedema

Colesevelam

78. Which of the following is the brand name for colesevelam?

a. Welchol
b. Gilenya
c. Plaquenil
d. Nipride

79. Colesevelam belongs to which of the following pharmacologic classes?

a. PCSK9 inhibitor
b. Statin
c. Fibrate
d. Bile acid sequestrant

80. Which of the following administration techniques applies to colesevelam?

a. Take with food and a liquid.
b. Avoid dairy products.
c. Take on an empty stomach.
d. Avoid antacids.

Conjugated estrogens-medroxyprogesterone acetate

81. Which of the following is a brand name for conjugated estrogens-medroxyprogester-one acetate?

a. Imdur
b. Florinef
c. Prempro
d. Menest

82. Conjugated estrogens-medroxyprogesterone acetate is indicated for the treatment and/or prevention of all but which of the following?

a. Menopausal symptoms
b. Breast cancer prevention
c. Vaginal dryness
d. Osteoporosis prevention

83. Conjugated estrogens-medroxyprogesterone acetate is available in which of the following dosage forms?

a. Oral tablet
b. Topical gel
c. Topical cream
d. Transdermal patch

Cyanocobalamin

84. Which of the following is a brand name for cyanocobalamin?

a. Cyanokit
b. Flurox
c. Sarafem
d. Nasocobal

85. Cyanocobalamin is indicated for the treatment of which of the following conditions?

a. Magnesium deficiency
b. Vitamin B_{12} deficiency
c. Vitamin D deficiency
d. Folic acid deficiency

86. Cyanocobalamin is available in all but which of the following dosage forms?

a. Oral tablet
b. Injection solution
c. Oral film
d. Nasal solution

Cyclobenzaprine

87. Which of the following is a brand name for cyclobenzaprine?

a. Flexeril
b. Eulexin
c. Norflex
d. Mobic

88. Cyclobenzaprine belongs to which of the following pharmacologic classes?

a. Anticonvulsant
b. Skeletal muscle relaxant
c. Analgesic
d. Sedative

89. Cyclobenzaprine is available in which of the following oral tablet strengths?

a. 2.5 mg
b. 10 mg
c. 15 mg
d. 20 mg

Cyclosporine

90. Which of the following is a brand name for cyclosporine?

a. Maxipime
b. Xiidra
c. Altace
d. Restasis

91. Cyclosporine is indicated for the treatment of which of the following conditions?

a. Dry eye
b. Macular degeneration
c. Glaucoma
d. Bacterial conjunctivitis

Dabigatran

92. Which of the following is the brand name for dabigatran?

a. Remeron
b. Megace
c. Pradaxa
d. Alupent

93. Dabigatran belongs to which of the following pharmacologic classes?

a. Antiplatelet agent
b. Anticoagulant
c. Platelet-stimulating agent
d. Thrombolytic

94. Dabigatran is available in which of the following dosage forms?

a. Intravenous solution
b. Oral tablet
c. Subcutaneous solution
d. Oral capsule

95. Which of the following is the most appropriate dosing for dabigatran when used to reduce the risk of stroke in patients with nonvalvular atrial fibrillation?

a. 75 mg once daily
b. 150 mg once daily
c. 150 mg twice daily
d. 300 mg twice daily

Desonide

96. Which of the following is a brand name for desonide?

a. Desonate
b. Nolvadex
c. Metvixia
d. Carac

97. Desonide belongs to which of the following pharmacologic classes?

a. Astringent
b. Corticosteroid
c. Antibiotic
d. Antifungal

98. Desonide is available in all but which of the following dosage forms?

a. Topical ointment
b. Topical gel
c. Topical cream
d. Topical solution

Desvenlafaxine

99. Which of the following is a brand name for desvenlafaxine?

a. Minocin
b. Effexor
c. Pristiq
d. Corgard

100. Desvenlafaxine belongs to which of the following pharmacologic classes?

a. Antidepressant
b. Diuretic
c. Antipsychotic
d. Immunosuppressant

101. Desvenlafaxine is available in which of the following dosage forms?

a. Oral solution
b. Oral tablet
c. Transdermal patch
d. Oral capsule

Dexamethasone

102. Which of the following is a brand name for dexamethasone?

a. Raptiva
b. Decadron
c. Rythmol
d. Lazanda

103. Dexamethasone belongs to which of the following pharmacologic classes?

a. Corticosteroid
b. Antihypertensive
c. Anticonvulsant
d. GI stimulant

104. Which of the following administration techniques applies to dexamethasone?

a. Do not use with nitrates.
b. Take 1 hour before meals or 2 hours after.
c. Avoid concomitant administration with dairy products.
d. Take with food.

Dexlansoprazole

105. Which of the following is a brand name for dexlansoprazole?

a. Lantus
b. Anaprox
c. Neudexta
d. Dexilant

106. Dexlansoprazole belongs to which of the following pharmacologic classes?

a. PPI
b. Thiazolidinedione
c. COX-2 inhibitor
d. Alpha-glucosidase inhibitor

107. Which of the following is the most appropriate dosing for dexlansoprazole when used for the treatment of GERD?

a. 30 mg once daily
b. 30 mg three times daily
c. 60 mg once daily
d. 60 mg twice daily

Dexmethylphenidate

108. Which of the following is the brand name for dexmethylphenidate?

a. Seroquel
b. Parnate
c. Focalin
d. Mysoline

109. Dexmethylphenidate belongs to which of the following pharmacologic classes?

a. Hypnotic
b. CNS stimulant
c. Antispasmodic
d. Antihistamine

110. Dexmethylphenidate is indicated for the treatment of which of the following conditions?

a. ADHD
b. Bipolar disorder
c. Narcolepsy
d. Depression

Diazepam

111. Which of the following is a brand name for diazepam?

a. Dapsone
b. Adalat CC
c. Procan
d. Valium

112. Diazepam belongs to which of the following pharmacologic classes?

a. Skeletal muscle relaxant
b. Antianxiety agent
c. Antihypertensive
d. Antiemetic

113. Diazepam is available in all but which of the following oral tablet strengths?

a. 2.5 mg
b. 5 mg
c. 10 mg
d. 15 mg

114. Diazepam has a black box warning regarding concomitant use with which of the following classes of medications?

a. Opioids
b. Cephalosporins
c. Antiarrhythmics
d. Barbiturates

Diclofenac

115. Which of the following is a brand name for diclofenac?

a. Stendra
b. Dilaudid
c. Albenza
d. Voltaren

116. Diclofenac belongs to which of the following pharmacologic classes?

a. Salicylate
b. Vasodilator
c. NSAID
d. Aromatase inhibitor

117. Diclofenac is available in all but which of the following dosage forms?

a. Topical gel
b. Transdermal patch
c. Ophthalmic ointment
d. Oral tablet

Dicyclomine

118. Which of the following is a brand name for dicyclomine?

a. Bentyl
b. Activase
c. Zyrtec
d. Tazorac

119. Dicyclomine belongs to which of the following pharmacologic classes?

a. Gastric antisecretory
b. Anticholinergic
c. Antidiuretic hormone
d. Antiemetic

120. Dicyclomine is indicated for the treatment of which of the following conditions?

a. Irritable bowel syndrome
b. Psychosis
c. Overactive bladder
d. Allergic conjunctivitis

121. Dicyclomine may cause all but which of the following adverse effects?

a. Decreased sweating
b. Nausea
c. Blurred vision
d. Salivation

Digoxin

122. Which of the following is a brand name for digoxin?

a. Prevacid
b. Tysabri
c. Quinidex
d. Lanoxin

123. Digoxin belongs to which of the following pharmacologic classes?

a. Calcimimetic
b. Antiarrhythmic
c. Laxative
d. Antianginal agent

124. Digoxin is indicated for the treatment of which of the following conditions?

a. Stroke
b. Bradycardia
c. Congestive heart failure
d. Peripheral artery disease

125. All but which of the following symptoms can be signs of digoxin toxicity?

a. Liver failure
b. Nausea
c. Delirium
d. Blurred or "yellow" vision

Diltiazem

126. Which of the following is a brand name for diltiazem?

a. Zenzedi
b. Pentasa
c. Rozerem
d. Cartia XT

127. Diltiazem belongs to which of the following pharmacologic classes?

a. SSRI
b. Calcium channel blocker
c. ACE inhibitor
d. Potassium-sparing diuretic

128. Diltiazem is indicated for the treatment of all but which of the following conditions?

a. Stable angina
b. Congestive heart failure
c. Hypertension
d. Atrial arrhythmia

Diphenoxylate-atropine

129. Which of the following is the brand name for diphenoxylate-atropine?

a. Topamax
b. Norco
c. Lomotil
d. Elitek

130. Diphenoxylate-atropine belongs to which of the following pharmacologic classes?

a. Antidiarrheal
b. Nasal decongestant
c. Antacid
d. Antirheumatic agent

131. Diphenoxylate-atropine belongs to which of the following DEA Schedules?

a. Schedule II
b. Schedule III
c. Schedule IV
d. Schedule V

132. Diphenoxylate-atropine is contraindicated in patients with which of the following conditions?

a. Ulcerative colitis
b. *C. difficile* infection
c. Chron's disease
d. Irritable bowel syndrome

Divalproex sodium

133. Which of the following is a brand name for divalproex sodium?

a. Depakote
b. Victoza
c. Renflexis
d. Lofibra

134. Divalproex sodium belongs to which of the following pharmacologic classes?

a. Inotropic agent
b. Antiparkinson agent
c. Anticonvulsant
d. Antipsychotic

135. Divalproex sodium has a black box warning regarding the risk of all but which of the following?

a. Pancreatitis
b. QT prolongation
c. Hepatotoxicity
d. Teratogenicity

136. All but which of the following are adverse effects that may occur with the use of divalproex sodium?

a. Tremor
b. Gingival hyperplasia
c. Alopecia
d. Weight gain

Donepezil

137. Which of the following is the brand name for donepezil?

a. Arcapta
b. Mirapex
c. Zarontin
d. Aricept

138. Donepezil belongs to which of the following pharmacologic classes?

a. Cholinesterase inhibitor
b. 5-HT$_3$ receptor antagonist
c. Incretin mimetic
d. mTOR inhibitor

139. Donepezil is indicated for the treatment of which of the following conditions?

a. Peptic ulcer disease
b. Angina
c. Alzheimer's disease
d. Rheumatoid arthritis

Dorzolamide-timolol

140. Which of the following is the brand name for dorzolamide-timolol?

a. Cosopt
b. Ocuflox
c. Azopt
d. ReoPro

141. Dorzolamide-timolol is a combination of which of the following classes of medications?

a. Carbonic anhydrase inhibitor and miotic
b. Carbonic anhydrase inhibitor and beta-blocker
c. Prostaglandin analog and beta-blocker
d. Alpha$_2$-agonist and miotic

142. Dorzolamide-timolol is indicated for the treatment of which of the following conditions?

a. Hypertension
b. Schizophrenia
c. COPD
d. Glaucoma

Doxazosin

143. Which of the following is the brand name for doxazosin?

a. Glucophage
b. Diprivan
c. Cardura
d. Rocephin

144. Doxazosin belongs to which of the following pharmacologic classes?

a. Alpha$_1$-blocker
b. Calcium channel blocker
c. Vasodilator
d. Alpha$_2$-agonist

145. Doxazosin is indicated for the treatment of which of the following conditions?

a. Pulmonary arterial hypertension
b. Gout
c. Insomnia
d. BPH

Doxepin

146. Which of the following is a brand name for doxepin?

a. Lopid
b. Azasan
c. Silenor
d. Anzemet

147. Doxepin belongs to which of the following pharmacologic classes?

a. Tricyclic antidepressant
b. Bile acid sequestrant
c. MAO inhibitor
d. $P2Y_{12}$ inhibitor

148. Doxepin inhibits the reuptake of which of the following neurotransmitters?

a. Norepinephrine and dopamine
b. Serotonin and dopamine
c. Histamine and glutamate
d. Serotonin and norepinephrine

Doxycycline

149. Which of the following is a brand name for doxycycline?

a. Questran
b. Vibramycin
c. Inderal XL
d. Elestrin

150. Doxycycline belongs to which of the following pharmacologic classes?

a. Penicillin antibiotic
b. Monobactam antibiotic
c. Tetracycline antibiotic
d. Sulfonamide antibiotic

151. Doxycycline is indicated for the treatment of all but which of the following conditions?

a. Endocarditis
b. Acne
c. Rocky Mountain spotted fever
d. Anthrax exposure

Duloxetine

152. Which of the following is a brand name for duloxetine?

a. Ziagen
b. Cymbalta
c. Azulfidine
d. Endocet

153. Duloxetine belongs to which of the following pharmacologic classes?

a. Bisphosphonate
b. SSRI
c. Aromatase inhibitor
d. SNRI

154. Duloxetine is available in which of the following dosage forms?

a. Oral solution
b. Intramuscular solution
c. Oral capsule
d. Topical gel

Dutasteride

155. Which of the following is the brand name for dutasteride?

a. Avodart
b. Rapaflo
c. Gralise
d. Crestor

156. Dutasteride belongs to which of the following pharmacologic classes?

a. H_2 receptor antagonist
b. 5-alpha reductase inhibitor
c. Alpha$_2$-agonist
d. SGLT-2 inhibitor

157. Dutasteride is indicated for the treatment of which of the following conditions?

a. BPH
b. Hyperkalemia
c. Constipation
d. Erectile dysfunction

ANSWER KEY

1. B
A brand name for calcitriol is Rocaltrol.

2. D
Calcitriol is classified as a vitamin D analog.

3. A
Among other conditions, calcitriol is indicated for the treatment of hypocalcemia in patients on chronic renal dialysis.

4. C
A brand name for carbamazepine is Tegretol.

5. D
Carbamazepine is classified as an anticonvulsant.

6. A
Carbamazepine has a black box warning regarding the risk of aplastic anemia, agranulocytosis, and dermatologic reactions such as toxic epidermal necrolysis and Stevens-Johnson syndrome. Carbamazepine does not have a black box warning regarding the risk of pulmonary toxicity.

7. D
A brand name for carbidopa-levodopa is Sinemet.

8. C
Carbidopa-levodopa is classified as an antiparkinson agent.

9. A
The absorption of carbidopa-levodopa can be decreased by iron.

10. B
A brand name for carisoprodol is Soma.

11. C
Carisoprodol is classified as a skeletal muscle relaxant.

12. A
Carisoprodol is available as an oral tablet.

13. D
The brand name for carvedilol is Coreg.

14. B
Carvedilol is classified as an antihypertensive.

15. D
Carvedilol blocks alpha$_1$-, beta$_1$-, and beta$_2$-receptors.

16. A
Carvedilol should be taken with food to minimize the risk of orthostatic hypotension.

17. B
The brand name for cefdinir is Omnicef.

18. D
Cefdinir is classified as a cephalosporin antibiotic.

19. C
Cefdinir is available as an oral capsule, as well as an oral suspension.

20. A
The brand name for cefuroxime is Ceftin.

21. D
Cefuroxime is classified as an antibiotic.

22. C
Cefuroxime is available in 250 mg oral tablets, as well as 500 mg.

23. A
The brand name for celecoxib is Celebrex.

24. B
Celecoxib is classified as an NSAID.

25. A
Celecoxib is available as an oral capsule.

26. D
Celecoxib has a black box warning regarding the risk of cardiovascular thrombotic events, such as myocardial infarction and stroke, as well as gastrointestinal events such as a bleeding, ulceration and perforation of the stomach or intestines. Celecoxib does not have a black box warning regarding the risk of heart failure, myelosuppression, or oto-toxicity.

27. B
A brand name for cephalexin is Keflex.

28. C
Cephalexin is classified as an antibiotic.

29. D
Cephalexin is available in 250 mg, 500 mg, and 750 mg oral capsules, as well as 333 mg oral capsules. Cephalexin is not available in 1,000 mg oral capsules.

30. A
A brand name for chlorhexidine is Peridex.

31. B
Chlorhexidine is classified as an antibiotic.

32. B
The most appropriate dosing for chlorhexidine when used as an oral rinse for the prevention of gingivitis is to swish for 30 seconds with 15 mL twice daily.

33. D
Chlorhexidine may cause tooth discoloration when used as an oral rinse.

34. C
The brand name for chlorthalidone is Thalitone.

35. A
Chlorthalidone is classified as a thiazide-related diuretic.

36. D
Chlorthalidone is available as an oral tablet.

37. A
A brand name for cholecalciferol is Delta D3.

38. B
Cholecalciferol is available as an oral capsule, oral liquid, and oral tablet, as well as a chewable tablet. Cholecalciferol is not available as a subcutaneous solution.

39. B
Cholecaciferol 50,000 units is typically dosed once a week for the treatment of vitamin D deficiency.

40. D
A brand name for ciprofloxacin is Cipro.

41. C
Ciprofloxacin is classified as a fluoroquinolone antibiotic.

42. A
Among other dosage forms, ciprofloxacin is available as an oral tablet, otic solution, and ophthalmic solution. Ciprofloxacin is not available as an intramuscular suspension.

43. D
Ciprofloxacin has a black box warning regarding the risk of tendon rupture.

44. B
The brand name for ciprofloxacin-dexamethasone is Ciprodex.

45. B
Ciprofloxacin-dexamethasone is indicated for the treatment of otitis externa, as well as acute otitis media in patients with tympanostomy tubes.

46. C
Ciprofloxacin-dexamethasone is available as an otic suspension.

47. D
The brand name for citalopram is Celexa.

48. B
Citalopram is classified as an antidepressant.

49. A
Among other adverse effects, citalopram may cause QT prolongation.

50. C
The highest strength available for citalopram oral tablets is 40 mg.

51. B
The brand name for clarithromycin is Biaxin.

52. D
Clarithromycin is classified as a macrolide antibiotic.

53. C
Clarithromycin is available in an oral suspension, as well as an oral tablet.

54. A
A brand name for clindamycin is Cleocin.

55. D
Clindamycin is classified as an antibiotic.

56. B
Among other dosage forms, clindamycin is available as a topical lotion, intravenous solution, and topical gel. Clindamycin is not available as an oral tablet.

57. C
Clindamycin has a black box warning regarding the risk of *Clostridium difficile*-associated diarrhea (CDAD).

58. A
A brand name for clobetasol is Temovate.

59. D
Clobetasol is classified as a corticosteroid.

60. B
Among other dosage forms, clobetasol is available as a topical cream.

61. C
The brand name for clonazepam is Klonopin.

62. A
Clonazepam is classified as a benzodiazepine.

63. C
Clonazepam belongs to DEA Schedule IV.

64. D
A brand name for clonidine is Catapres.

65. A
Clonidine is classified as an alpha$_2$-agonist.

66. B
Among other conditions, clonidine is indicated for the treatment of hypertension.

67. D
The brand name for clopidogrel is Plavix.

68. C
Clopidogrel is classified as an antiplatelet agent.

69. C
Clopidogrel is available in 75 mg oral tablets, as well as 300 mg.

70. A
The effectiveness of clopidogrel will be diminished in patients that have reduced function of the CYP2C19 enzyme, which converts clopidogrel to its active metabolite.

71. D
The brand name for clotrimazole-betamethasone is Lotrisone.

72. B
Clotrimazole-betamethasone is a combination of an antifungal and corticosteroid.

73. C
Clotrimazole-betamethasone is available as a topical cream, as well as a topical lotion.

74. A
A brand name for colchicine is Colcrys.

75. B
Colchicine is classified as an antigout agent.

76. D
Colchicine is available as an oral tablet.

77. C
In addition to other adverse effects, colchicine may cause gastrointestinal effects, such as diarrhea, nausea, and vomiting.

78. A
The brand name for colesevelam is Welchol.

79. D
Colesevelam is classified as a bile acid sequestrant.

80. A
Colesevelam should be taken with food and a liquid to prevent constipation.

81. C
A brand name for conjugated estrogens-medroxyprogesterone acetate is Prempro.

82. B
Conjugated estrogens-medroxyprogesterone acetate is indicated for the treatment of menopausal symptoms and vaginal dryness, and the prevention of osteoporosis. Conjugated estrogens-medroxyprogesterone acetate is not indicated for breast cancer prevention.

83. A
Conjugated estrogens-medroxyprogesterone acetate is available as an oral tablet.

84. D
A brand name for cyanocobalamin is Nasocobal.

85. B
Cyanocobalamin is indicated for the treatment of vitamin B_{12} deficiency.

86. C
Among other dosage forms, cyanocobalamin is available as an oral tablet, injection solution, and nasal solution. Cyanocobalamin is not available as an oral film.

87. A
A brand name for cyclobenzaprine is Flexeril.

88. B
Cyclobenzaprine is classified as a skeletal muscle relaxant.

89. B
Cyclobenzaprine is available in 10 mg oral tablets, as well as 5 mg and 7.5 mg.

90. D
A brand name for cyclosporine is Restasis.

91. A
Among other indications, cyclosporine is indicated for the treatment of dry eye.

92. C
The brand name for dabigatran is Pradaxa.

93. B
Dabigatran is classified as an anticoagulant.

94. D
Dabigatran is available as an oral capsule.

95. C
The most appropriate dosing for dabigatran when used to reduce the risk of stroke in patients with nonvalvular atrial fibrillation is 150 mg twice daily.

96. A
A brand name for desonide is Desonate.

97. B
Desonide is classified as a corticosteroid.

98. D
Desonide is available as a topical ointment, gel and cream, in addition to a topical foam and lotion. Desonide is not available as a topical solution.

99. C
A brand name for desvenlafaxine is Pristiq.

100. A
Desvenlafaxine is classified as an antidepressant.

101. B
Desvenlafaxine is available as an oral tablet.

102. B
A brand name for dexamethasone is Decadron.

103. A
Dexamethasone is classified as a corticosteroid.

104. D
Dexamethasone should be taken with food to help prevent GI upset.

105. D
A brand name for dexlansoprazole is Dexilant.

106. A
Dexlansoprazole is classified as a PPI.

107. A

The most appropriate dosing for dexlansoprazole when used for the treatment of GERD is 30 mg once daily.

108. C

The brand name for dexmethylphenidate is Focalin.

109. B

Dexmethylphenidate is classified as a CNS stimulant.

110. A

Dexmethylphenidate is indicated for the treatment of ADHD.

111. D

A brand name for diazepam is Valium.

112. B

Diazepam is classified as an antianxiety agent.

113. D

Diazepam is available in 2.5 mg, 5 mg, and 10 mg oral tablets. Diazepam is not available in 15 mg oral tablets.

114. A

Diazepam has a black box warning regarding concomitant use with opioids due to the risk of sedation, respiratory depression, coma or death.

115. D

A brand name for diclofenac is Voltaren.

116. C

Diclofenac is classified as an NSAID.

117. C

Among other dosage forms, diclofenac is available as a topical gel, transdermal patch, and oral tablet. Diclofenac is not available as an ophthalmic ointment.

118. A

A brand name for dicyclomine is Bentyl.

119. B

Dicyclomine is classified as an anticholinergic.

120. A

Dicyclomine is indicated for the treatment of irritable bowel syndrome.

121. D

Among other adverse effects, dicyclomine may cause decreased sweating, nausea, blurred vision, and dry mouth.

122. D
A brand name for digoxin is Lanoxin.

123. B
Digoxin is classified as an antiarrhythmic.

124. C
In addition to atrial fibrillation, digoxin is indicated for the treatment of congestive heart failure.

125. A
Nausea, delirium, and blurred or "yellow vision" are some of the signs of digoxin toxicity. Liver failure is not a sign of digoxin toxicity.

126. D
A brand name for diltiazem is Cartia XT.

127. B
Diltiazem is classified as a calcium channel blocker.

128. B
Among other conditions, diltiazem is indicated for the treatment of stable angina, hypertension, and atrial arrhythmia. Diltiazem is not indicated for the treatment of congestive heart failure.

129. C
The brand name for diphenoxylate-atropine is Lomotil.

130. A
Diphenoxylate-atropine is classified as an antidiarrheal.

131. D
Diphenoxylate-atropine belongs to DEA Schedule V.

132. B
Diphenoxylate-atropine is contraindicated in patients with *C. difficile* infection due to the risk of toxic megacolon.

133. A
A brand name for divalproex sodium is Depakote.

134. C
Divalproex sodium is classified as an anticonvulsant.

135. B
Divalproex sodium has a black box warning regarding the risk of pancreatitis, hepatotoxicity, and teratogenicity. Divalproex sodium does not have a black box warning regarding the risk of QT prolongation.

136. B
Tremor, alopecia, and weight gain are some of the adverse effects that may occur with the use of divalproex sodium. Gingival hyperplasia is not associated with divalproex sodium.

137. D
The brand name for donepezil is Aricept.

138. A
Donepezil is classified as a cholinesterase inhibitor.

139. C
Donepezil is indicated for the treatment of Alzheimer's disease.

140. A
The brand name for dorzolamide-timolol is Cosopt.

141. B
Dorzolamide-timolol is a combination of a carbonic anhydrase inhibitor and beta-blocker.

142. D
Dorzolamide-timolol is indicated for the treatment of glaucoma.

143. C
The brand name for doxazosin is Cardura.

144. A
Doxazosin is classified as an alpha$_1$-blocker.

145. D
Doxazosin is indicated for the treatment of BPH.

146. C
A brand name for doxepin is Silenor.

147. A
Doxepin is classified as a tricyclic antidepressant.

148. D
Doxepin inhibits the reuptake of serotonin and norepinephrine. Doxepin also blocks acetylcholine and histamine receptors. Doxepin does not inhibit the reuptake of dopamine or glutamate.

149. B
A brand name for doxycycline is Vibramycin.

150. C
Doxycycline is classified as a tetracycline antibiotic.

151. A

Among other conditions, doxycycline is indicated for the treatment of acne, Rocky Mountain spotted fever, and anthrax exposure. Doxycycline is not indicated for the treatment of endocarditis.

152. B

A brand name for duloxetine is Cymbalta.

153. D

Duloxetine is classified as an SNRI.

154. C

Duloxetine is available as an oral capsule.

155. A

The brand name for dutasteride is Avodart.

156. B

Dutasteride is classified as a 5-alpha reductase inhibitor.

157. A

Dutasteride is indicated for the treatment of BPH.

DRUGS E – G

QUESTIONS

Enalapril

1. Which of the following is a brand name for enalapril?

a. Onglyza
b. Vasotec
c. Atelvia
d. Lyrica

2. Enalapril belongs to which of the following pharmacologic classes?

a. ACE inhibitor
b. SGLT-2 inhibitor
c. Neurokinin-1 receptor antagonist
d. Beta-blocker

3. Enalapril is contraindicated in patients who develop which of the following conditions while taking it?

a. Dysgeusia
b. Cough
c. Angioedema
d. Hypotension

Enoxaparin

4. Which of the following is the brand name for enoxaparin?

a. Lovenox
b. Tekturna
c. Namenda
d. Pyridium

5. Enoxaparin belongs to which the following pharmacologic classes?

a. Immunosuppressant
b. Platelet-stimulating agent
c. GI stimulant
d. Anticoagulant

6. All but which of the following are appropriate administration techniques for the sub-cutaneous administration of enoxaparin?

a. Rub the injection site to prevent bruising.
b. Insert the needle at a 90-degree angle.
c. Rotate injection sites.
d. Do not expel the air bubble in the syringe.

7. The use of enoxaparin is contraindicated in patients with which of the following conditions?

a. Protein C deficiency
b. Atrial fibrillation
c. Heparin-induced thrombocytopenia
d. Asthma

Epinephrine

8. Which of the following is a brand name for epinephrine?

a. Brevibloc
b. Adipex-P
c. Nicotrol
d. EpiPen

9. Epinephrine belongs to which of the following pharmacologic classes?

a. Antiandrogen
b. Anaphylaxis agent
c. Skeletal muscle relaxant
d. Corticosteroid

10. Epinephrine administered intramuscularly should be injected into which part of the body?

a. Arm
b. Buttock
c. Thigh
d. Abdomen

Epoetin alfa

11. Which of the following is a brand name for epoetin alfa?

a. Saphris
b. Levaquin
c. Procrit
d. Tranxene-T

12. Epoetin alfa belongs to which of the following pharmacologic classes?

a. Hematopoietic agent
b. Tocolytic agent
c. Thrombolytic agent
d. Antithyroid agent

13. Which of the following is the preferred route of administration for epoetin alfa in most patients?

a. Oral
b. Intramuscular
c. Sublingual
d. Subcutaneous

Ergocalciferol

14. Which of the following is a brand name for ergocalciferol?

a. Calciferol
b. Actonel
c. Ferate
d. Cycloset

15. Ergocalciferol is also known as which of the following vitamins?

a. Vitamin A
b. Vitamin B_6
c. Vitamin D_2
d. Vitamin D_3

16. Ergocalciferol is available in all but which of the following dosage forms?

a. Oral capsule
b. Oral solution
c. Oral tablet
d. Oral film

Erythromycin

17. Which of the following is a brand name for erythromycin?

a. Videx
b. Ery-Tab
c. Antivert
d. Frova

18. Erythromycin belongs to which of the following pharmacologic classes?

a. Macrolide antibiotic
b. Penicillin antibiotic
c. Ketolide antibiotic
d. Cephalosporin antibiotic

19. Erythromycin may cause which of the following adverse effects?

a. Hypotension
b. Thrombocytopenia
c. QT prolongation
d. Hyperkalemia

Escitalopram

20. Which of the following is the brand name for escitalopram?

a. Revlimid
b. Actos
c. Osmitrol
d. Lexapro

21. Escitalopram belongs to which of the following pharmacologic classes?

a. SSRI
b. Tricyclic antidepressant
c. Bisphosphonate
d. Calcineurin inhibitor

22. Escitalopram is indicated for the treatment of which of the following conditions?

a. Generalized anxiety disorder
b. Dementia
c. Insomnia
d. Neuropathic pain

23. Escitalopram is available in which of the following oral tablet strengths?

a. 2.5 mg
b. 10 mg
c. 25 mg
d. 40 mg

Esomeprazole

24. Which of the following is the brand name for esomeprazole?

a. Latuda
b. Nexterone
c. Kombiglyze XR
d. Nexium

25. Esomeprazole belongs to which of the following pharmacologic classes?

a. Chloride channel activator
b. PPI
c. Cytoprotective agent
d. Antacid

26. Esomeprazole is indicated for the treatment of which of the following conditions?

a. GERD
b. Constipation
c. Diverticulitis
d. *C. difficile* infection

27. Esomeprazole is most effective if taken at which of the following times of day?

a. 1 hour before breakfast
b. 2 hours after lunch
c. 30 minutes after dinner
d. Before bedtime

Estradiol

28. Which of the following is a brand name for estradiol?

a. Forteo
b. Vivelle-Dot
c. Femara
d. Norvir

29. Estradiol belongs to which of the following pharmacologic classes?

a. Growth hormone
b. Aromatase inhibitor
c. Prolactin inhibitor
d. Endocrine agent

30. Estradiol can be used for the prevention of which of the following conditions?

a. Osteoporosis
b. Dementia
c. Stroke
d. Breast cancer

Conjugated Estrogens

31. Which of the following is the brand name for conjugated estrogens?

a. Estring
b. Antara
c. Premarin
d. Trintellix

32. Conjugated estrogens are available in which of the following dosage forms?

a. Topical gel
b. Vaginal cream
c. Vaginal ring
d. Transdermal patch

33. All but which of the following statements regarding the use conjugated estrogens are
   true?

a. Therapy should be initiated at the lowest dose.
b. Adverse effects can be alleviated by changing the method of administration.
c. Therapy should be used for the shortest duration possible.
d. Therapy does not need to be tapered upon discontinuation.

Eszopiclone

34. Which of the following is the brand name for eszopiclone?

a. Lunesta
b. Vesicare
c. Omnaris
d. Zelapar

35. Eszopiclone belongs to which of the following pharmacologic classes?

a. Melatonin receptor agonist
b. Benzodiazepine
c. Hypnotic
d. Dopamine agonist

36. Which of the following is the maximum daily dose for eszopiclone?

a. 3 mg
b. 6 mg
c. 8 mg
d. 10 mg

Etanercept

37. Which of the following is the brand name for etanercept?

a. Phenergan
b. Enbrel
c. Suprax
d. Orencia

38. Etanercept belongs to which of the following pharmacologic classes?

a. Factor Xa inhibitor
b. Interleukin-1 inhibitor
c. VMAT2 inhibitor
d. Tumor necrosis factor inhibitor

39. Etanercept is indicated for the treatment of all but which of the following conditions?

a. Osteoarthritis
b. Psoriatic arthritis
c. Plaque psoriasis
d. Rheumatoid arthritis

40. Patients should be evaluated for which of the following prior to initiation of therapy with etanercept?

a. Hepatitis C
b. Osteoporosis
c. Tuberculosis
d. Kidney failure

Ethinyl estradiol-desogestrel

41. Which of the following is a brand name for ethinyl estradiol-desogestrel?

a. Errin
b. Kariva
c. Avandia
d. Xulane

42. Ethinyl estradiol-desogestrel belongs to which of the following pharmacologic classes?

a. Oral contraceptive
b. Somatostatin analog
c. Gonadotropin
d. Prolactin inhibitor

Ethinyl estradiol-drosperinone

43. Which of the following is a brand name for ethinyl estradiol-drosperinone?

a. Estrogel
b. Aviane
c. Restoril
d. Yaz

44. Ethinyl estradiol-drosperinone can increase patient levels of which of the following?

a. Calcium
b. Potassium
c. Magnesium
d. Sodium

Ethinyl estradiol-etonogestrel

45. Which of the following is the brand name for ethinyl estradiol-etonogestrel?

a. Demadex
b. Gianvi
c. NuvaRing
d. Alora

46. Ethinyl estradiol-etonogestrel is inserted vaginally and left in place continuously for _____ for contraception.

a. 3 weeks
b. 4 weeks
c. 8 weeks
d. 12 weeks

Ethinyl estradiol-levonorgestrel

47. Which of the following is a brand name for ethinyl estradiol-levonorgestrel?

a. Mircette
b. Activella
c. Januvia
d. Seasonique

48. The levels of ethinyl estradiol-levonorgestrel can be decreased by all but which of the following?

a. Phenytoin
b. Furosemide
c. Rifampin
d. St. John's wort

Ethinyl estradiol-norethindrone

49. Which of the following is a brand name for ethinyl estradiol-norethindrone?

a. Premphase
b. Lo Loestrin Fe
c. Serzone
d. Avapro

50. Ethinyl estradiol-norethindrone suppresses the levels of which of the following hormones?

a. Luteinizing hormone and follicle-stimulating hormone
b. Estrogen and luteinizing hormone
c. Follicle-stimulating hormone and estrogen
d. Progesterone and human chorionic gonadotropin

Ethinyl estradiol-norgestimate

51. Which of the following is a brand name for ethinyl estradiol-norgestimate?

a. Jinteli
b. Axiron
c. Ortho-Cyclen
d. Provera

52. Ethinyl estradiol-norgestimate would be contraindicated in which of the following patients?

a. A 35-year-old female that is HIV positive
b. A 30-year-old female that has a history of gestational diabetes
c. A 37-year-old female that smokes
d. A 28-year-old female with uterine fibroids

Etodolac

53. Which of the following is the brand name for etodolac?

a. Diastat
b. Lodine
c. Toprol XL
d. Herceptin

54. Etodolac belongs to which of the following pharmacologic classes?

a. Antibiotic
b. Sulfonylurea
c. Phosphate binder
d. NSAID

55. Etodolac is available in which of the following dosage forms?

a. Oral tablet
b. Subcutaneous solution
c. Topical gel
d. Transdermal patch

Exenatide

56. Which of the following is a brand name for exenatide?

a. Bydureon
b. Taxol
c. Reclast
d. Compazine

57. Exenatide belongs to which of the following pharmacologic classes?

a. Thiazolidinedione
b. H_2 receptor antagonist
c. GLP-1 receptor agonist
d. Anticholinergic

58. Exenatide is available in which of the following dosage forms?

a. Nasal spray
b. Subcutaneous injection
c. Oral capsule
d. Oral solution

59. Exenatide is contraindicated in patients with a history of which of the following?

a. Medullary thyroid carcinoma
b. Stevens-Johnson syndrome
c. Hepatitis
d. Angioedema

Ezetimibe

60. Which of the following is the brand name for ezetimibe?

a. Pravachol
b. Viread
c. Noxafil
d. Zetia

61. Ezetimibe belongs to which of the following pharmacologic classes?

a. Antihyperlipidemic
b. Anticonvulsant
c. Serotonin receptor agonist
d. Thiazide diuretic

62. Ezetimibe is available in which of the following oral tablet strengths?

a. 5 mg
b. 10 mg
c. 20 mg
d. 30 mg

Famotidine

63. Which of the following is the brand name for famotidine?

a. Zovirax
b. Cardene
c. Ultiva
d. Pepcid

64. Famotidine belongs to which of the following pharmacologic classes?

a. DPP-4 inhibitor
b. H_2 receptor antagonist
c. Bronchodilator
d. Bile acid sequestrant

65. Which of the following is the highest strength that is available for famotidine oral tablets?

a. 10 mg
b. 20 mg
c. 40 mg
d. 80 mg

Febuxostat

66. Which of the following is the brand name for febuxostat?

a. Uloric
b. Chantix
c. Selzentry
d. Multaq

67. Febuxostat belongs to which of the following pharmacologic classes?

a. PDE-5 inhibitor
b. COX-2 inhibitor
c. Antidepressant
d. Xanthine oxidase inhibitor

68. Febuxostat decreases the production of which of the following?

a. Cholesterol
b. Uric acid
c. Histamine
d. Thyroxine

69. Febuxostat is available in which of the following dosage forms?

a. Oral tablet
b. Transdermal patch
c. Topical cream
d. Subcutaneous solution

Felodipine

70. Which of the following is the brand name for felodipine?

a. Elmiron
b. Zymar
c. Plendil
d. Uribel

71. Felodipine belongs to which of the following pharmacologic classes?

a. $5HT_1$ agonist
b. Calcium channel blocker
c. $Alpha_1$-blocker
d. Analgesic

72. Felodipine is indicated for the treatment of which of the following conditions?

a. Migraine
b. Thromboembolism
c. Erectile dysfunction
d. Hypertension

Fenofibrate

73. Which of the following is a brand name for fenofibrate?

a. Tricor
b. Normodyne
c. Lybrel
d. Protonix

74. Fenofibrate belongs to which of the following pharmacologic classes?

a. Antidiabetic
b. Antirheumatic agent
c. Antihyperlipidemic
d. Anticoagulant

75. The risk of rhabdomyolysis is increased when fenofibrate is used concomitantly with which of the following classes of medication?

a. Alpha-glucosidase inhibitors
b. Statins
c. Thiazide diuretics
d. Bisphosphonates

Fentanyl

76. Which of the following is a brand name for fentanyl?

a. Duragesic
b. Glyset
c. PegIntron
d. Calan

77. Fentanyl belongs to which of the following pharmacologic classes?

a. Protease inhibitor
b. P2Y$_{12}$ inhibitor
c. Beta$_1$-blocker
d. Opioid analgesic

78. Fentanyl is available in all but which of the following dosage forms?

a. Oral tablet
b. Injection solution
c. Topical ointment
d. Oral lozenge

79. Fentanyl transdermal patches should be changed every _____ hours.

a. 24 hours
b. 36 hours
c. 72 hours
d. 96 hours

Fidaxomicin

80. Which of the following is the brand name for fidaxomicin?

a. Dificid
b. Plexion
c. Monurol
d. Valtrex

81. Fidaxomicin belongs to which of the following pharmacologic classes?

a. Tetracycline antibiotic
b. Monobactam antibiotic
c. Aminoglycoside antibiotic
d. Macrolide antibiotic

82. Which of the following is the most appropriate dosing of fidaxomicin for the treatment of *C. difficile*-associated diarrhea?

a. 200 mg once daily
b. 200 mg twice daily
c. 400 mg once daily
d. 400 mg twice daily

Finasteride

83. Which of the following is a brand name for finasteride?

a. Proscar
b. Revatio
c. Zyflo CR
d. Levsin

84. Finasteride belongs to which of the following pharmacologic classes?

a. COMT inhibitor
b. Alpha$_2$-blocker
c. 5-alpha reductase inhibitor
d. Glutamate antagonist

85. Finasteride is indicated for the treatment of which of the following conditions?

a. Epilepsy
b. Alopecia
c. Migraines
d. Bipolar disorder

86. Which of the following is the most appropriate dosing of finasteride for the treatment of BPH?

a. 1 mg once daily
b. 1 mg twice daily
c. 5 mg once daily
d. 5 mg twice daily

Fluconazole

87. Which of the following is the brand name for fluconazole?

a. Diflucan
b. Acular
c. Tirosint
d. Brilinta

88. Fluconazole belongs to which of the following pharmacologic classes?

a. Anabolic steroid
b. Gastric antisecretory
c. Antiemetic
d. Antifungal

89. Fluconazole is available in all but which of the following oral tablet strengths?

a. 50 mg
b. 100 mg
c. 200 mg
d. 250 mg

Fluocinonide

90. Which of the following is a brand name for fluocinonide?

a. Vanos
b. Topicort
c. Zestoretic
d. Capex

91. Fluocinonide belongs to which of the following pharmacologic classes?

a. Diuretic
b. Androgen inhibitor
c. Corticosteroid
d. Antitussive

92. Fluocinonide is available in all but which of the following dosage forms?

a. Topical cream
b. Topical foam
c. Topical gel
d. Topical ointment

Fluoxetine

93. Which of the following is a brand name for fluoxetine?

a. Symbyax
b. Aloprim
c. Venofer
d. Prozac

94. Fluoxetine belongs to which of the following pharmacologic classes?

a. SSRI
b. Hypnotic
c. Sulfonylurea
d. ACE inhibitor

95. Fluoxetine is indicated for the treatment of all but which of the following conditions?

a. Obsessive compulsive disorder
b. Panic disorder
c. ADHD
d. Major depressive disorder

96. Fluoxetine may cause all but which of the following adverse effects?

a. CNS stimulation
b. Sexual dysfunction
c. Nausea
d. Crystalluria

Fluticasone

97. Which of the following is a brand name for fluticasone?

a. Viberzi
b. Flonase
c. Apokyn
d. Reglan

98. Fluticasone belongs to which of the following pharmacologic classes?

a. Corticosteroid
b. Antineoplastic
c. Expectorant
d. Antianxiety agent

99. Fluticasone is available in all but which of the following dosage forms?

a. Topical cream
b. Inhalation aerosol
c. Nasal spray
d. Ophthalmic solution

Fluticasone-salmeterol

100. Which of the following is a brand name for fluticasone-salmeterol?

a. Myfortic
b. Picato
c. Advair Diskus
d. Flovent HFA

101. Fluticasone-salmeterol belongs to which of the following pharmacologic classes?

a. CNS stimulant
b. Antiasthma agent
c. Immunosuppressant
d. Antirheumatic agent

102. Fluticasone-salmeterol is available in which of the following dosage forms?

a. Inhalation aerosol
b. Oral solution
c. Nebulizer solution
d. Nasal spray

103. Patients should rinse their mouth with water after using fluticasone-salmeterol for the prevention of which of the following adverse effects?

a. Cough
b. Hoarseness
c. Dysphonia
d. Oral candidiasis

Folic acid

104. Which of the following is a brand name for folic acid?

a. Nutropin AQ
b. Folbic
c. Folacin-800
d. Mephyton

105. Folic acid is the synthetic form of which of the following vitamins?

a. Vitamin B_6
b. Vitamin B_9
c. Vitamin D_2
d. Vitamin K

106. Women of child-bearing age should have adequate intake of folic acid to prevent which of the following birth defects?

a. Down syndrome
b. Heart defects
c. Blindness
d. Neural tube defects

107. Folic acid can be used to help reduce the adverse effects associated with which of the following medications?

a. Methotrexate
b. Amiodarone
c. Hydroxychloroquine
d. Indomethacin

Fosinopril

108. Which of the following is the brand name for fosinopril?

a. Belsomra
b. Monopril
c. Prinivil
d. Synercid

109. Fosinopril belongs to which of the following pharmacologic classes?

a. Antihypertensive
b. Analgesic
c. Antiviral
d. Anticoagulant

110. Fosinopril is available in which of the following dosage forms?

a. Oral capsule
b. Transdermal patch
c. Intravenous solution
d. Oral tablet

Furosemide

111. Which of the following is the brand name for furosemide?

a. Propecia
b. Lasix
c. Edecrin
d. Avelox

112. Furosemide belongs to which of the following pharmacologic classes?

a. Antihypertensive
b. Skeletal muscle relaxant
c. Antianginal agent
d. Antiandrogen

113. Furosemide acts on which of the following parts of the nephron?

a. Collecting duct
b. Distal convoluted tubule
c. Proximal tubule
d. Loop of Henle

114. Furosemide may cause all but which of the following adverse effects?

a. Hypocalcemia
b. Photosensitivity
c. Hypoglycemia
d. Ototoxicity

Gabapentin

115. Which of the following is a brand name for gabapentin?

a. Levitra
b. Angiomax
c. Cytotec
d. Neurontin

116. Gabapentin belongs to which of the following pharmacologic classes?

a. Aldosterone antagonist
b. Anticonvulsant
c. Antiparkinson agent
d. Vasodilator

117. Gabapentin is indicated for the treatment of which of the following conditions?

a. Postherpetic neuralgia
b. Opioid withdrawal
c. Migraine
d. Gastric ulcer

118. Gabapentin oral capsules are available in all but which of the following strengths?

a. 100 mg
b. 300 mg
c. 400 mg
d. 600 mg

Gemfibrozil

119. Which of the following is the brand name for gemfibrozil?

a. Norvasc
b. Tindamax
c. Lopid
d. Zanaflex

120. Gemfibrozil belongs to which of the following pharmacologic classes?

a. Fibrate
b. ARB
c. Bile acid sequestrant
d. Beta$_2$-agonist

121. Gemfibrozil is available in which of the following oral tablet strengths?

a. 300 mg
b. 400 mg
c. 600 mg
d. 1,000 mg

122. Which of the following is the most appropriate administration of gemfibrozil?

a. Once daily 1 hour before breakfast
b. Once daily at bedtime on an empty stomach
c. Twice daily with breakfast and dinner
d. Twice daily 30 minutes before breakfast and dinner

Glimepiride

123. Which of the following is the brand name for glimepiride?

a. Lotensin
b. Amaryl
c. Fragmin
d. Trivora

124. Glimepiride belongs to which of the following pharmacologic classes?

a. Antidiabetic
b. Antihypertensive
c. Antianginal agent
d. Antipyretic

125. Glimepiride is available in which of the following dosage forms?

a. Inhalation aerosol
b. Oral capsule
c. Oral tablet
d. Subcutaneous solution

126. Which of the following is the most appropriate administration of glimepiride?

a. Once daily on an empty stomach
b. Once daily with first main meal of the day
c. Once daily at bedtime
d. Twice daily 1 hour after breakfast and dinner

Glipizide

127. Which of the following is the brand name for glipizide?

a. Fosamax
b. Duetact
c. Arixtra
d. Glucotrol

128. Glipizide belongs to which of the following pharmacologic classes?

a. Sulfonylurea
b. Thiazolidinedione
c. Alpha-glucosidase inhibitor
d. GLP-1 agonist

129. Glipizide should not be used in combination with which of the following types of antidiabetic agents?

a. Biguanide
b. Amylin analog
c. Meglitinide
d. Alpha-glucosidase inhibitor

Glyburide

130. Which of the following is a brand name for glyburide?

a. Lysodren
b. Micronase
c. Azasan
d. Protopic

131. Glyburide belongs to which of the following pharmacologic classes?

a. Urinary antispasmodic
b. Antifungal
c. Analgesic
d. Antidiabetic

132. Glyburide should be used with caution in which of the following patient populations?

a. Elderly
b. African Americans
c. Females
d. Asthmatics

Guanfacine

133. Which of the following is a brand name for guanfacine?

a. Unithroid
b. Desyrel
c. Intuniv
d. Tracleer

134. Guanfacine belongs to which of the following pharmacologic classes?

a. Fluoroquinolone antibiotic
b. ACE inhibitor
c. Benzodiazepine
d. Alpha$_2$-agonist

135. Guanfacine is indicated for the treatment of which of the following conditions?

a. ADHD
b. Heart failure
c. COPD
d. Alzheimer's disease

136. Which of the following administration techniques applies to extended-release guanfacine tablets?

a. Take with at least 8 oz. of water.
b. Do not take with a high-fat meal.
c. Do not take with antacids or iron.
d. Take with food or milk.

Guaifenesin-codeine

137. Which of the following is a brand name for guaifenesin-codeine?

a. Cheratussin AC
b. Fioricet
c. Hycodan
d. Beconase AQ

138. Guaifenesin-codeine is a combination of a/an _____ and a/an _____.

a. antiemetic; antitussive
b. antipyretic; expectorant
c. antitussive; decongestant
d. expectorant; antitussive

139. Guaifenesin-codeine is available in which of the following dosage forms?

a. Oral lozenge
b. Oral solution
c. Oral capsule
d. Oral tablet

140. Guaifenesin-codeine belongs to which of the following DEA Schedules?

a. Schedule II
b. Schedule III
c. Schedule IV
d. Schedule V

ANSWER KEY

1. B
A brand name for enalapril is Vasotec.

2. A
Enalapril is classified as an ACE inhibitor.

3. C
Enalapril is contraindicated in patients who develop angioedema while taking it.

4. A
The brand name for enoxaparin is Lovenox.

5. D
Enoxaparin is classified as an anticoagulant.

6. A
When administering enoxaparin subcutaneously, patients should insert the needle at a 90-degree angle and rotate injection sites. The air bubble in the syringe should not be expelled, and patients should avoid rubbing the injection site as this can cause bruising.

7. C
The use of enoxaparin is contraindicated in patients with a history of heparin-induced thrombocytopenia in the past 100 days or in the presence of circulating antibodies.

8. D
A brand name for epinephrine is EpiPen.

9. B
Epinephrine is classified as an anaphylaxis agent.

10. C
Epinephrine administered intramuscularly should be injected in the middle of the outer thigh.

11. C
A brand name for epoetin alfa is Procrit.

12. A
Epoetin alfa is classified as a hematopoietic agent.

13. D
The preferred route of administration for epoetin alfa in most patients is subcutaneous injection. The intravenous route is preferred in patients with chronic kidney disease on hemodialysis.

14. A
A brand name for ergocalciferol is Calciferol.

15. C
Ergocalciferol is also known as vitamin D_2.

16. D
Ergocalcalciferol is available as an oral capsule, oral solution, and oral tablet. Ergocalciferol is not available as an oral film.

17. B
A brand name for erythromycin is Ery-Tab.

18. A
Erythromycin is classified as a macrolide antibiotic.

19. C
Among other adverse effects, erythromycin may cause QT prolongation.

20. D
The brand name for escitalopram is Lexapro.

21. A
Escitalopram is classified as an SSRI.

22. A
In addition to major depressive disorder, escitalopram is indicated for the treatment of generalized anxiety disorder.

23. B
Escitalopram is available in 10 mg oral tablets, as well as 5 mg and 20 mg.

24. D
The brand name for esomeprazole is Nexium.

25. B
Esomeprazole is classified as a PPI.

26. A
Among other conditions, esomeprazole is indicated for the treatment of GERD.

27. A
Esomeprazole only inhibits proton pumps that are actively secreting acid, therefore it is most effective if taken 1 hour before a meal, usually breakfast.

28. B
A brand name for estradiol is Vivelle-Dot.

29. D
Estradiol is classified as an endocrine agent.

30. A

Estradiol can be used for the prevention of osteoporosis in postmenopausal women.

31. C

The brand name for conjugated estrogens is Premarin.

32. B

Conjugated estrogens are available as a vaginal cream, as well as an oral tablet and injection solution.

33. D

Conjugated estrogens and other forms of hormone-replacement therapy should be initiated at the lowest dose and used for the shortest duration possible. Adverse effects can be alleviated by changing the method of administration. Therapy should be tapered before discontinuation to prevent the recurrence of hot flashes.

34. A

The brand name for eszopiclone is Lunesta.

35. C

Eszopiclone is classified as a hypnotic.

36. A

The maximum daily dose for eszopiclone is 3 mg.

37. B

The brand name for etanercept is Enbrel.

38. D

Etanercept is classified as a tumor necrosis factor inhibitor.

39. A

Among other indications, etanercept is indicated for the treatment of psoriatic arthritis, plaque psoriasis, and rheumatoid arthritis. Etanercept is not indicated for the treatment of osteoarthritis.

40. C

Patients should be evaluated for tuberculosis prior to initiation of therapy with etanercept.

41. B

A brand name for ethinyl estradiol-desogestrel is Kariva.

42. A

Ethinyl estradiol-desogestrel is classified as an oral contraceptive.

43. D

A brand name for ethinyl estradiol-drosperinone is Yaz.

44. B
Ethinyl estradiol-drosperinone can increase patients' potassium levels.

45. C
The brand name for ethinyl estradiol-etonogestrel is NuvaRing.

46. A
Ethinyl estradiol-etonogestrel is inserted vaginally and left in place continuously for 3 weeks for contraception.

47. D
A brand name for ethinyl estradiol-levonorgestrel is Seasonique.

48. B
Among other medications, the levels of ethinyl estradiol-levonorgestrel can be decreased by phenytoin, rifampin, and St. John's wort. The levels of ethinyl estradiol-levonorgestrel are not affected by furosemide.

49. B
A brand name for ethinyl estradiol-norethindrone is Lo Loestrin Fe.

50. A
Ethinyl estradiol-norethindrone suppresses the levels of luteinizing hormone and follicle-stimulating hormone.

51. C
A brand name for ethinyl estradiol-norgestimate is Ortho-Cyclen.

52. C
Combined oral contraceptives, such as ethinyl estradiol-norgestimate, are contraindicated in females that are over 35 years old and smoke due to the increased risk of stroke or myocardial infarction.

53. B
The brand name for etodolac is Lodine.

54. D
Etodolac is classified as an NSAID.

55. A
Etodolac is available as an oral tablet, as well as an oral capsule.

56. A
A brand name for exenatide is Bydureon.

57. C
Exenatide is classified as a GLP-1 agonist.

58. B
Exenatide is available as a subcutaneous injection.

59. A
Exenatide is contraindicated in patients with a personal or family history of medullary thyroid carcinoma and in patients with Multiple Endocrine Neoplasia syndrome type 2.

60. D
The brand name for ezetimibe is Zetia.

61. A
Ezetimibe is classified as an antihyperlipidemic.

62. B
Ezetimibe is available in 10 mg oral tablets.

63. D
The brand name for famotidine is Pepcid.

64. B
Famotidine is classified as an H_2 receptor antagonist.

65. C
The highest strength that is available for famotidine oral tablets is 40 mg.

66. A
The brand name for febuxostat is Uloric.

67. D
Febuxostat is classified as a xanthine oxidase inhibitor.

68. B
Febuxostat decreases the production of uric acid.

69. A
Febuxostat is available as an oral tablet.

70. C
The brand name for felodipine is Plendil.

71. B
Felodipine is classified as a calcium channel blocker.

72. D
Felodipine is indicated for the treatment of hypertension.

73. A
A brand name for fenofibrate is Tricor.

74. C
Fenofibrate is classified as an antihyperlipidemic.

75. B
The risk of rhabdomyolysis is increased when fenofibrate is used concomitantly with statins.

76. A
A brand name for fentanyl is Duragesic.

77. D
Fentanyl is classified as an opioid analgesic.

78. C
Among other dosage forms, fentanyl is available as an oral tablet, injection solution, and oral lozenge. Fentanyl is not available as a topical ointment.

79. C
Fentanyl transdermal patches should be changed every 72 hours.

80. A
The brand name for fidaxomicin is Dificid.

81. D
Fidaxomicin is classified as a macrolide antibiotic.

82. B
The most appropriate dosing of fidaxomicin for the treatment of *C. difficile*-associated diarrhea is 200 mg twice daily for 10 days.

83. A
A brand name for finasteride is Proscar.

84. C
Finasteride is classified as a 5-alpha reductase inhibitor.

85. B
Among other conditions, finasteride is indicated for the treatment of alopecia.

86. C
The most appropriate dosing of finasteride for the treatment of BPH is 5 mg once daily.

87. A
The brand name for fluconazole is Diflucan.

88. D
Fluconazole is classified as an antifungal.

89. D
Fluconazole is available in 50 mg, 100 mg, and 200 mg oral tablets, as well as 150 mg oral tablets. Fluconazole is not available in 250 mg oral tablets.

90. A
A brand name for fluocinonide is Vanos.

91. C
Fluocinonide is classified as a corticosteroid.

92. B
Among other dosage forms, fluocinonide is available as a topical cream, topical gel, and topical ointment. Fluocinonide is not available as a topical foam.

93. D
A brand name for fluoxetine is Prozac.

94. A
Fluoxetine is classified as an SSRI.

95. C
Among other conditions, fluoxetine is indicated for the treatment of obsessive compulsive disorder, panic disorder and major depressive disorder. Fluoxetine is not indicated for the treatment of ADHD.

96. D
Among other adverse effects, fluoxetine may cause CNS stimulation, sexual dysfunction, and nausea. Fluoxetine is not associated with crystalluria.

97. B
A brand name for fluticasone is Flonase.

98. A
Fluticasone is classified as a corticosteroid.

99. D
Among other dosage forms, fluticasone is available as a topical cream, inhalation aerosol, and nasal spray. Fluticasone is not available as an ophthalmic solution.

100. C
A brand name for fluticasone-salmeterol is Advair Diskus.

101. B
Fluticasone-salmeterol is classified as an antiasthma agent.

102. A
Fluticasone-salmeterol is available as an inhalation aerosol, and a dry powder for oral inhalation.

103. D

Patients should rinse their mouth with water after using fluticasone-salmeterol for the prevention of oral candidiasis.

104. C

A brand name for folic acid is Folacin-800.

105. B

Folic acid is the synthetic form of vitamin B_9.

106. D

Women of child-bearing age should have adequate intake of folic acid to prevent neural tube defects.

107. A

Folic acid can be used to help reduce the adverse effects associated with methotrexate.

108. B

The brand name for fosinopril is Monopril.

109. A

Fosinopril is classified as an antihypertensive.

110. D

Fosinopril is available as an oral tablet.

111. B

The brand name for furosemide is Lasix.

112. A

Furosemide is classified as an antihypertensive.

113. D

Furosemide acts on the ascending limb of the Loop of Henle.

114. C

Among other adverse effects, furosemide may cause hypocalcemia, photosensitivity, hyperglycemia, and ototoxicity.

115. D

A brand name for gabapentin is Neurontin.

116. B

Gabapentin is classified as an anticonvulsant.

117. A

Gabapentin is indicated for the treatment of postherpetic neuralgia, as well as partial seizures.

118. D
Gabapentin oral capsules are available in 100 mg, 300 mg, and 400 mg. Gabapentin 600 mg is available in oral tablets.

119. C
The brand name for gemfibrozil is Lopid.

120. A
Gemfibrozil is classified as a fibrate.

121. C
Gemfibrozil is available in 600 mg oral tablets.

122. D
The most appropriate administration of gemfibrozil is twice daily 30 minutes before breakfast and dinner.

123. B
The brand name for glimepiride is Amaryl.

124. A
Glimepiride is classified as an antidiabetic.

125. C
Glimepiride is available as an oral tablet.

126. B
The most appropriate administration of glimepiride is once daily with breakfast or the first main meal of the day.

127. D
The brand name for glipizide is Glucotrol.

128. A
Glipizide is classified as a sulfonylurea.

129. C
Glipizide should not be used with combination with a meglitinide due to their similar mechanism of action.

130. B
A brand name for glyburide is Micronase.

131. D
Glyburide is classified as an antidiabetic.

132. A
Glyburide should be used with caution in elderly patients due to the risk of prolonged hypoglycemia.

133. C
A brand name for guanfacine is Intuniv.

134. D
Guanfacine is classified as an alpha$_2$-agonist.

135. A
Guanfacine is indicated for the treatment of ADHD.

136. B
Extended-release guanfacine tablets should be not be taken with a high-fat meal due to increased absorption.

137. A
A brand name for guaifenesin-codeine is Cheratussin AC.

138. D
Guaifenesin-codeine is a combination of an expectorant and an antitussive.

139. B
Guaifenesin-codeine is available as an oral solution.

140. D
Guaifenesin-codeine belongs to DEA Schedule V.

DRUGS H – L

QUESTIONS

Haloperidol

1. Which of the following is the brand name for haloperidol?

a. Tegretol
b. Kapvay
c. Haldol
d. Rhinocort

2. Haloperidol belongs to which of the following pharmacologic classes?

a. Antipsychotic
b. Smoking cessation agent
c. Antivertigo agent
d. Antihypertensive

3. Which of the following potential adverse effects of haloperidol can be irreversible?

a. Dystonia
b. Akathisia
c. Pseudoparkinsonism
d. Tardive dyskinesia

4. How often is haloperidol decanoate typically administered?

a. Once a week
b. Every 2 weeks
c. Once a month
d. Every 6 months

Hydralazine

5. Which of the following is a brand name for hydralazine?

a. Apresoline
b. Daytrana
c. Tenormin
d. Prosom

6. Hydralazine belongs to which of the following pharmacologic classes?

a. Renin inhibitor
b. Vasodilator
c. Potassium-sparing diuretic
d. mTOR inhibitor

7. Hydralazine may cause which of the following adverse effects?

a. Edema
b. Alopecia
c. Gingival hyperplasia
d. Lupus-like syndrome

Hydrochlorothiazide

8. Which of the following is a brand name for hydrochlorothiazide?

a. Klonopin
b. Aldomet
c. Microzide
d. Integrilin

9. Hydrochlorothiazide belongs to which of the following pharmacologic classes?

a. Diuretic
b. Platelet-stimulating agent
c. Beta-agonist
d. GI stimulant

10. Hydrochlorothiazide may cause all but which of the following adverse effects?

a. Hypomagnesemia
b. Hyponatremia
c. Hypokalemia
d. Hypocalcemia

11. Hydrochlorothiazide is contraindicated in patients that are allergic to which of the following types of medications?

a. Opioids
b. Sulfonamides
c. Penicillins
d. NSAIDs

Hydrocodone-acetaminophen

12. Which of the following is a brand name for hydrocodone-acetaminophen?

a. Norco
b. Lovenox
c. Dolophine
d. Aclovate

13. Hydrocodone-acetaminophen belongs to which of the following pharmacologic classes?

a. Antianxiety agent
b. Sedative
c. Opioid analgesic
d. Antipsychotic

14. Hydrocodone-acetaminophen may cause all but which of the following adverse effects?

a. Nausea
b. Urticaria
c. Sedation
d. Diarrhea

Hydrocortisone

15. Which of the following is a brand name for hydrocortisone?

a. Verdeso
b. Westcort
c. Dermazone
d. Temovate

16. Hydrocortisone belongs to which of the following pharmacologic classes?

a. Corticosteroid
b. Antifungal
c. Antihistamine
d. Local anesthetic

17. All but which of the following local adverse effects of hydrocortisone are reversible?

a. Steroid rosacea
b. Striae
c. Acne
d. Skin atrophy

Hydromorphone

18. Which of the following is a brand name for hydromorphone?

a. Lioresal
b. Opana
c. Exjade
d. Dilaudid

19. Hydromorphone belongs to which of the following pharmacologic classes?

a. Skeletal muscle relaxant
b. SNRI
c. Anticonvulsant
d. Opioid analgesic

20. Hydromorphone belongs to which of the following DEA Schedules?

a. Schedule II
b. Schedule III
c. Schedule IV
d. Schedule V

Hydroxychloroquine

21. Which of the following is the brand name for hydroxychloroquine?

a. Elavil
b. Doryx
c. Plaquenil
d. Neulasta

22. Hydroxychloroquine belongs to which of the following pharmacologic classes?

a. Inotropic agent
b. Antimalarial agent
c. Antigout agent
d. Analgesic

23. Hydroxychloroquine is indicated for the treatment of all but which of the following conditions?

a. Lupus
b. Rheumatoid arthritis
c. Malaria
d. Hepatitis C

24. Hydroxychloroquine may cause which of the following adverse effects?

a. Pneumonitis
b. Retinal toxicity
c. Pancreatitis
d. Hypotension

Hydroxyzine

25. Which of the following is a brand name for hydroxyzine?

a. Atarax
b. Lialda
c. Deltasone
d. Zonalon

26. Hydroxyzine belongs to which of the following pharmacologic classes?

a. Corticosteroid
b. Bronchodilator
c. Hypnotic
d. Antihistamine

27. Hydroxyzine is indicated for the treatment of which of the following conditions?

a. Constipation
b. Pruritis
c. Dry eye
d. Anemia

Hyoscyamine

28. Which of the following is a brand name for hyoscyamine?

a. Zelnorm
b. Maxzide
c. Levsin
d. Edarbyclor

29. Hyoscyamine belongs to which of the following pharmacologic classes?

a. Anticholinergic
b. Anticoagulant
c. Antibiotic
d. CNS stimulant

30. Hyoscyamine is indicated for the treatment of which of the following conditions?

a. Glaucoma
b. Hypothyroidism
c. Asthma
d. IBS

Ibandronate

31. Which of the following is the brand name for ibandronate?

a. Tikosyn
b. Boniva
c. Seroquel
d. Exalgo

32. Ibandronate belongs to which of the following pharmacologic classes?

a. Bisphosphonate
b. Factor Xa inhibitor
c. SERM
d. Antiandrogen

33. Ibandronate is available in which of the following oral tablet strengths?

a. 75 mg
b. 150 mg
c. 175 mg
d. 200 mg

34. Ibandronate may cause which of the following adverse effects?

a. Cholelithiasis
b. Thomboembolic events
c. Hypercalcemia
d. Ostenecrosis of the jaw

Ibuprofen

35. Which of the following is a brand name for ibuprofen?

a. Motrin
b. Norpace
c. Ditropan XL
d. Lozol

36. Ibuprofen belongs to which of the following pharmacologic classes?

a. Beta-blocker
b. Corticosteroid
c. NSAID
d. Phosphate binder

37. Which of the following is the highest daily recommended prescription dose of ibuprofen for adults?

a. 1,200 mg
b. 2,400 mg
c. 3,200 mg
d. 3,600 mg

38. Pregnant women should avoid the use of ibuprofen due to the risk of which of the following adverse effects?

a. Congenital heart defects
b. Premature closure of the fetal ductus arteriosus
c. Neural tube defects
d. Intrauterine growth retardation

Imiquimod

39. Which of the following is a brand name for imiquimod?

a. Strattera
b. Elidel
c. Claravis
d. Aldara

40. Imiquimod belongs to which of the following pharmacologic classes?

a. Immune modulator
b. Antifungal
c. Antineoplastic
d. Debriding agent

41. Imiquimod is indicated for the treatment of all but which of the following conditions?

a. Genital warts
b. Actinic keratosis
c. Psoriasis
d. Superficial basal cell carcinoma

42. Imiquimod is available in which of the following dosage forms?

a. Oral tablet
b. Topical cream
c. Shampoo
d. Topical solution

Indomethacin

43. Which of the following is a brand name for indomethacin?

a. Levbid
b. Symlin
c. Indocin
d. Extavia

44. Indomethacin belongs to which of the following pharmacologic classes?

a. NSAID
b. Anticholinergic
c. Opioid analgesic
d. Muscle relaxant

45. Indomethacin is indicated for the treatment of pain associated with which of the following conditions?

a. Migraines
b. Fibromylagia
c. Muscle spasms
d. Gout

Insulin aspart

46. Which of the following is a brand name for insulin aspart?

a. Afrezza
b. Novolog
c. Peridex
d. Soliqua

47. Insulin aspart is a _____-acting insulin.

a. long-acting
b. rapid-acting
c. short-acting
d. intermediate-acting

Insulin detemir

48. Which of the following is a brand name for insulin detemir?

a. Basaglar KwikPen
b. Tanzeum
c. Colcrys
d. Levemir FlexTouch

49. Insulin detemir is a _____-acting insulin.

a. long-acting
b. short-acting
c. intermediate-acting
d. rapid-acting

50. Pens or vials of insulin detemir that are in use can be stored at room temperature for _____ days.

a. 14
b. 28
c. 42
d. 56

Insulin glargine

51. Which of the following is a brand name for insulin glargine?

a. Apidra
b. Qvar
c. Saxenda
d. Lantus

52. Insulin glargine is a _____-acting insulin.

a. short-acting
b. long-acting
c. rapid-acting
d. intermediate-acting

53. How often is insulin glargine typically dosed?

a. Three times a day
b. Once a day
c. Once a week
d. Twice a week

Regular human insulin

54. Which of the following is a brand name for regular human insulin?

a. Novolin R
b. Aggrenox
c. Toujeo SoloStar
d. Xultophy

55. Regular human insulin is a _____-acting insulin.

a. intermediate-acting
b. long-acting
c. short-acting
d. rapid-acting

56. Regular human insulin is typically dosed at which of the following times?

a. 30 minutes before a meal
b. 1 hour before a meal
c. 1 hour after a meal
d. 2 hours after a meal

Insulin lispro

57. Which of the following is a brand name for insulin lispro?

a. Humalog
b. Valtrex
c. Fiasp
d. Tresiba FlexTouch

58. Insulin lispro is a _____-acting insulin.

a. intermediate-acting
b. long-acting
c. short-acting
d. rapid-acting

59. Patients should rotate injection sites when administering insulin lispro to prevent which of the following?

a. Bruising
b. Infection
c. Lipohypertrophy
d. Extravasation

Ipratropium

60. Which of the following is a brand name for ipratropium?

a. Brovana
b. Atrovent HFA
c. Theocron
d. Ventolin HFA

61. Ipratropium belongs to which of the following pharmacologic classes?

a. Anticholinergic
b. Leukotriene receptor antagonist
c. Mast cell stabilizer
d. Beta$_2$-agonist

62. Ipratropium is indicated for the treatment of which of the following conditions?

a. Pneumonia
b. Sleep apnea
c. COPD
d. Pulmonary hypertension

Irbesartan

63. Which of the following is the brand name for irbesartan?

a. Zantac
b. Inspra
c. Lomaira
d. Avapro

64. Irbesartan belongs to which of the following pharmacologic classes?

a. Antiglaucoma agent
b. Antihypertensive
c. Decongestant
d. Antidiabetic

65. Levels of which of the following should be monitored in patients receiving irbesartan?

a. Uric acid
b. Blood glucose
c. Potassium
d. Sodium

Isosorbide mononitrate

66. Which of the following is a brand name for isosorbide mononitrate?

a. Digitek
b. Abilify
c. Soliris
d. Imdur

67. Isosorbide mononitrate belongs to which of the following pharmacologic classes?

a. Antianxiety agent
b. Antianginal agent
c. Bronchodilator
d. GI stimulant

68. Immediate release isosorbide mononitrate is typically dosed _____ times daily with _____ hours between doses.

a. 2; 7
b. 2; 10
c. 2; 12
d. 3; 8

69. Isosorbide mononitrate should not be used concomitantly with which of the following medications?

a. Propranolol
b. Clopidogrel
c. Tadalafil
d. Metformin

Ketoconazole

70. Which of the following is a brand name for ketoconazole?

a. Solodyn
b. Miacalcin
c. Atripla
d. Nizoral

71. Ketoconazole belongs to which of the following pharmacologic classes?

a. Antibiotic
b. Antifungal
c. Antineoplastic agent
d. Antihistamine

72. Topical ketoconazole is available in all but which of the following dosage forms?

a. Solution
b. Cream
c. Shampoo
d. Foam

Labetalol

73. Which of the following is a brand name for labetalol?

a. Trandate
b. Cogentin
c. Acticlate
d. Hepsera

74. Labetalol belongs to which of the following pharmacologic classes?

a. Analgesic
b. CNS stimulant
c. Antihypertensive
d. Antidepressant

75. Labetalol blocks all but which of the following receptors?

a. Alpha$_1$
b. Alpha$_2$
c. Beta$_1$
d. Beta$_2$

Lamotrigine

76. Which of the following is the brand name for lamotrigine?

a. Aerospan
b. Evista
c. Synarel
d. Lamictal

77. Lamotrigine belongs to which of the following pharmacologic classes?

a. Anticonvulsant
b. NSAID
c. Sedative
d. Antimigraine agent

78. A titration schedule is often followed when initiating therapy with lamotrigine to reduce the risk of which of the following adverse effects?

a. Hepatotoxicity
b. Hyponatremia
c. Skin rash
d. Aplastic anemia

79. Lamotrigine is available in which of the following dosage forms?

a. Oral solution
b. Oral tablet
c. Intramuscular suspension
d. Oral capsule

Lansoprazole

80. Which of the following is the brand name for lansoprazole?

a. Xyzal
b. Rexulti
c. Alocril
d. Prevacid

81. Lansoprazole belongs to which of the following pharmacologic classes?

a. PPI
b. Opioid antagonist
c. Tetracycline antibiotic
d. Calcium channel blocker

82. Lansoprazole can affect the absorption of all but which of the following?

a. Calcium
b. Vitamin B_{12}
c. Magnesium
d. Vitamin A

83. Which of the following is the highest strength that is available for lansoprazole oral capsules?

a. 15 mg
b. 20 mg
c. 30 mg
d. 40 mg

Latanoprost

84. Which of the following is the brand name for latanoprost?

a. Xalatan
b. Carbatrol
c. Singulair
d. Faslodex

85. Latanoprost belongs to which of the following pharmacologic classes?

a. Carbonic anhydrase inhibitor
b. Prostaglandin analog
c. Neuraminidase inhibitor
d. Anticonvulsant

86. Latanoprost is indicated for the treatment of which of the following conditions?

a. Osteoporosis
b. Peptic ulcer disease
c. Anxiety
d. Glaucoma

87. After opening, latanoprost may be stored at room temperature for _____ weeks.

a. 4 weeks
b. 6 weeks
c. 8 weeks
d. 12 weeks

Letrozole

88. Which of the following is the brand name for letrozole?

a. Hyosyne
b. Lipitor
c. Femara
d. Aredia

89. Letrozole belongs to which of the following pharmacologic classes?

a. Aromatase inhibitor
b. PPI
c. Alpha$_1$-blocker
d. Cholinergic agonist

90. Letrozole is indicated for the treatment of which of the following conditions in post-menopausal women?

a. Osteoporosis
b. Vaginal atrophy
c. Breast cancer
d. IBS

Levalbuterol

91. Which of the following is the brand name for levalbuterol?

a. Otovel
b. Dyazide
c. Antabuse
d. Xopenex

92. Levalbuterol belongs to which of the following pharmacologic classes?

a. COX-2 inhibitor
b. Beta$_2$-agonist
c. Neurokinin-1 receptor antagonist
d. Antiplatelet agent

93. Levalbuterol is indicated for the treatment of which of the following conditions?

a. Asthma
b. Allergic rhinitis
c. Erectile dysfunction
d. Overactive bladder

94. Levalbuterol may cause all but which of the following adverse effects?

a. Tremor
b. Bradycardia
c. Hyperglycemia
d. Cough

Levetiracetam

95. Which of the following is a brand name for levetiracetam?

a. Xanax
b. Casodex
c. Qnasl
d. Keppra

96. Levetiracetam belongs to which of the following pharmacologic classes?

a. Anticonvulsant
b. Antihyperlipidemic
c. Antidiarrheal
d. Antidiabetic

97. Immediate release levetiracetam tablets are typically dosed _____ time(s) daily.

a. one
b. two
c. three
d. four

Levocetirizine

98. Which of the following is the brand name for levocetirizine?

a. Emsam
b. Artane
c. Lopressor
d. Xyzal

99. Levocetirizine belongs to which of the following pharmacologic classes?

a. PDE-5 inhibitor
b. Chloride channel activator
c. H_1 antagonist
d. MAO-B inhibitor

100. Levocetirizine is available in which of the following oral tablet strengths?

a. 2.5 mg
b. 5 mg
c. 10 mg
d. 15 mg

Levofloxacin

101. Which of the following is a brand name for levofloxacin?

a. Luvox
b. Ultram
c. Bepreve
d. Levaquin

102. Levofloxacin belongs to which of the following pharmacologic classes?

a. Antidepressant
b. Corticosteroid
c. Antibiotic
d. Antifungal

103. Levofloxacin is available in all but which of the following oral tablet strengths?

a. 250 mg
b. 500 mg
c. 750 mg
d. 1,000 mg

104. Which of the following can decrease the absorption of levofloxacin?

a. Antacids
b. H_2 receptor antagonists
c. Antihistamines
d. Sulfonylureas

Levothyroxine

105. Which of the following is a brand name for levothyroxine?

a. Viramune
b. Levoxyl
c. BiDil
d. Eliquis

106. Levothyroxine belongs to which of the following pharmacologic classes?

a. Antidiabetic
b. Antihypertensive
c. Vasodilator
d. Thyroid product

107. Levothyroxine is which of the following hormones?

a. Synthetic T_3 and T_4
b. Synthetic T_3
c. Desiccated T_3 and T_4
d. Synthetic T_4

108. A patient may experience which of the following adverse effects if their dose of levothyroxine is too high?

a. Fatigue
b. Cold intolerance
c. Tachycardia
d. Weight gain

Lidocaine

109. Which of the following is a brand name for topical lidocaine?

a. Lidoderm
b. Patanase
c. Flector
d. Ifex

110. Topical lidocaine belongs to which of the following pharmacologic classes?

a. Anticonvulsant
b. Analgesic
c. Antiemetic
d. Antihypertensive

111. All but which of the following statements are true regarding the use of topical lido-caine patches?

a. The patches should be removed after 12 hours.
b. Do not cover the patches with a heating pad or electric blanket.
c. No more than 3 patches should be applied at one time.
d. The patches cannot be cut.

112. Lidocaine topical patches should be used with caution when used concomitantly with which of the following classes of medications?

a. Class I antiarrhythmics
b. Erythropoiesis-stimulating agents
c. Opioids
d. Monoclonal antibiodies

Linagliptan

113. Which of the following is the brand name for linagliptan?

a. Pulmicort
b. Zyclara
c. Tradjenta
d. Digox

114. Linagliptan belongs to which of the following pharmacologic classes?

a. Bile acid sequestrant
b. Xanthine oxidase inhibitor
c. Macrolide antibiotic
d. DPP-4 inhibitor

115. Linagliptan is indicated for the treatment of which of the following conditions?

a. Atrial fibrillation
b. Diabetes
c. Glaucoma
d. Hyperlipidemia

116. Linagliptan is available in which of the following oral tablet strengths?

a. 5 mg
b. 10 mg
c. 20 mg
d. 30 mg

Liraglutide

117. Which of the following is a brand name for liraglutide?

a. Urocit-K
b. Pacerone
c. Amerge
d. Victoza

118. Liraglutide belongs to which of the following pharmacologic classes?

a. Antiplatelet agent
b. GLP-1 receptor agonist
c. Aldosterone receptor antagonist
d. ACE inhibitor

119. Liraglutide is available in which of the following dosage forms?

a. Subcutaneous solution
b. Inhalation aerosol
c. Oral tablet
d. Topical cream

120. Liraglutide has a black box warning regarding the risk of which of the following?

a. Pulmonary fibrosis
b. Fatal bleeding
c. Venous thromboembolism
d. Thyroid C-cell tumors

Lisdexamfetamine

121. Which of the following is the brand name for lisdexamfetamine?

a. Prozac
b. Relistor
c. Vyvanse
d. Intermezzo

122. Lisdexamfetamine belongs to which of the following pharmacologic classes?

a. Antianxiety agent
b. Bronchodilator
c. Antidepressant
d. CNS stimulant

123. Lisdexamfetamine is indicated for the treatment of which of the following conditions?

a. Epilepsy
b. ADHD
c. Narcolepsy
d. Tourettte syndrome

124. Which of the following is the maximum recommended daily dose for lisdexamfetamine?

a. 70 mg
b. 100 mg
c. 120 mg
d. 140 mg

Lisinopril

125. Which of the following is a brand name for lisinopril?

a. Prinivil
b. Apriso
c. Ziac
d. Istalol

126. Lisinopril belongs to which of the following pharmacologic classes?

a. Vasopressin antagonist
b. Alpha-glucosidase inhibitor
c. ACE inhibitor
d. Statin

127. Lisinopril may cause all but which of the following adverse effects?

a. Dizziness
b. Hypokalemia
c. Angioedema
d. Cough

Lisinopril-hydrochlorothiazide

128. Which of the following is a brand name for lisinopril-hydrochlorothiazide?

a. Vimovo
b. Diovan
c. Zestoretic
d. Micardis HCT

129. Lisinopril-hydrochlorothiazide belongs to which of the following pharmacologic classes?

a. Antihypertensive
b. Bone resorption inhibitor
c. Antimigraine agent
d. Antigout agent

130. Lisinopril-hydrochlorothiazide is available in which of the following dosage forms?

a. Oral tablet
b. Transdermal patch
c. Oral capsule
d. Sublingual tablet

Lithium carbonate

131. Which of the following is a brand name for lithium carbonate?

a. Desogen
b. Astepro
c. Zomig
d. Lithobid

132. Lithium carbonate belongs to which of the following pharmacologic classes?

a. Antimanic agent
b. Antpsychotic
c. Smoking cessation agent
d. Anticonvulsant

133. All but which of the following can decrease lithium levels?

a. Caffeine
b. Increased salt intake
c. NSAIDs
d. Theophylline

Lorazepam

134. Which of the following is the brand name for lorazepam?

a. Demerol
b. Ativan
c. Protonix
d. Monodox

135. Lorazepam belongs to which of the following pharmacologic classes?

a. Meglitinide
b. Alpha$_1$-blocker
c. Protease inhibitor
d. Benzodiazepine

136. Lorazepam is indicated for the treatment of which of the following conditions?

a. Asthma
b. Schizophrenia
c. Anxiety
d. Pain

137. Lorazepam is available in all but which of the following oral tablet strengths?

a. 0.25 mg
b. 0.5 mg
c. 1 mg
d. 2 mg

Losartan

138. Which of the following is the brand name for losartan?

a. Paxil
b. Cozaar
c. Duricef
d. Acanya

139. Losartan belongs to which of the following pharmacologic classes?

a. ARB
b. Loop diuretic
c. H_2 receptor antagonist
d. SSRI

140. Losartan should be avoided in which of the following patient populations?

a. Hyperthyroid patients
b. Liver failure patients
c. Heart failure patients
d. Pregnant patients

Losartan-hydrochlorothiazide

141. Which of the following is the brand name for losartan-hydrochlorothiazide?

a. Lipofen
b. Hyzaar
c. Glucotrol XL
d. Elimite

142. Losartan-hydrochlorothiazide belongs to which of the following pharmacologic classes?

a. Antihypertensive
b. Antianginal agent
c. Antirheumatic agent
d. Antihyperlipidemic

143. Losartan-hydrochlorothiazide is available in which of the following dosage forms?

a. Oral capsule
b. Transdermal patch
c. Oral tablet
d. Nasal spray

Loteprednol

144. Which of the following is a brand name for loteprednol?

a. Dexilant
b. Adcirca
c. Edluar
d. Lotemax

145. Loteprednol belongs to which of the following pharmacologic classes?

a. Antibiotic
b. Corticosteroid
c. NSAID
d. Antipyretic

146. Loteprednol is indicated for the treatment of which of the following conditions?

a. Allergic conjunctivitis
b. Erectile dysfunction
c. GERD
d. Cough

Lovastatin

147. Which of the following is a brand name for lovastatin?

a. Jublia
b. Alinia
c. Soma
d. Mevacor

148. Lovastatin belongs to which of the following pharmacologic classes?

a. HMG-CoA reductase inhibitor
b. Macrolide antibiotic
c. mTOR inhibitor
d. Antiarrhythmic agent

149. Lovastatin is available in all but which of the following oral tablet strengths?

a. 10 mg
b. 20 mg
c. 30 mg
d. 40 mg

Lubiprostone

150. Which of the following is the brand name for lubiprostone?

a. Timoptic
b. Amitiza
c. Ella
d. Cimzia

151. Lubiprostone belongs to which of the following pharmacologic classes?

a. Calcium channel blocker
b. Potassium supplement
c. Renin inhibitor
d. Chloride channel activator

152. Lubiprostone is indicated for the treatment of which of the following conditions?

a. Constipation
b. Anemia
c. Depression
d. Smoking cessation

153. Which of the following administration techniques applies to lubiprostone?

a. Take with food and water.
b. Do not take at the same time as antacids and multivitamins.
c. Avoid taking with a high-fat meal.
d. Avoid alcohol.

Lurasidone

154. Which of the following is the brand name for lurasidone?

a. Bydureon
b. Nydrazid
c. Latuda
d. Pepcid

155. Lurasidone belongs to which of the following pharmacologic classes?

a. Skeletal muscle relaxant
b. Antipsychotic
c. Anticoagulant
d. Anticholingeric

156. All but which of the following may be adverse effects of lurasidone?

a. Nausea
b. Weight gain
c. Akathisia
d. Hypoglycemia

157. Lurasidone is available in which of the following dosage forms?

a. Oral tablet
b. Intramuscular solution
c. Subcutaneous solution
d. Oral solution

ANSWER KEY

1. C
The brand name for haloperidol is Haldol.

2. A
Haloperidol is classified as an antipsychotic.

3. D
Tardive dyskinesia is a potential adverse effect of haloperidol that can be irreversible.

4. C
Haloperidol decanoate is typically administered once a month.

5. A
A brand name for hydralazine is Apresoline.

6. B
Hydralazine is classified as a vasodilator.

7. D
Among other adverse effects, hydralazine may cause Lupus-like syndrome.

8. C
A brand name for hydrochlorothiazide is Microzide.

9. A
Hydrochlorothiazide is classified as a diuretic.

10. D
Among other adverse effects, hydrochlorothiazide may cause hypomagnesemia, hypo-natremia, hypokalemia, and hypercalcemia.

11. B
Hydrochlorothiazide is a sulfonamide derivative and is contraindicated in patients that are allergic to sulfonamides.

12. A
A brand name for hydrocodone-acetaminophen is Norco.

13. C
Hydrocodone-acetaminophen is classified as an opioid analgesic.

14. D
Among other adverse effects, hydrocodone-acetaminophen may cause nausea, urticaria, sedation, and constipation.

15. B
A brand name for hydrocortisone is Westcort.

16. A
Hydrocortisone is classified as a corticosteroid.

17. B
Steroid rosacea, acne, and skin atrophy are local side effects of hydrocortisone that are reversible. Striae is a local side effect of hydrocortisone that is irreversible.

18. D
A brand name for hydromorphone is Dilaudid.

19. D
Hydromorphone is classified as an opioid analgesic.

20. A
Hydromorphone belongs to DEA Schedule II.

21. C
The brand name for hydroxychloroquine is Plaquenil.

22. B
Hydroxychloroquine is classified as an antimalarial agent.

23. D
Hydroxychloroquine is indicated for the treatment of Lupus, rheumatoid arthritis, and malaria. Hydroxychloroquine is not indicated for the treatment of hepatitis C.

24. B
Among other adverse effects, hydroxychloroquine may cause retinal toxicity.

25. A
A brand name for hydroxyzine is Atarax.

26. D
Hydroxyzine is classified as an antihistamine.

27. B
Among other indications, hydroxyzine is indicated for the treatment of pruritis.

28. C
A brand name for hyoscyamine is Levsin.

29. A
Hyoscyamine is classified as an anticholinergic.

30. D
Among other indications, hyoscyamine is indicated for the treatment of IBS.

31. B
The brand name for ibandronate is Boniva.

32. A
Ibandronate is classified as a bisphosphonate.

33. B
Ibandronate is available in 150 mg oral tablets.

34. D
Ibandronate may cause osteonecrosis of the jaw.

35. A
A brand name for ibuprofen is Motrin.

36. C
Ibuprofen is classified as an NSAID.

37. C
The highest daily recommended prescription dose of ibuprofen for adults is 3,200 mg.

38. B
Pregnant women should avoid the use of ibuprofen, particularly during the third trimester, due to the risk of premature closure of the fetal ductus arteriosus.

39. D
A brand name for imiquimod is Aldara.

40. A
Imiquimod is classified as an immune modulator.

41. C
Imiquimod is indicted for the treatment of genital warts, actinic keratosis, and superficial basal cell carcinoma. Imiquimod is not indicated for the treatment of psoriasis.

42. B
Imquimod is available as a topical cream.

43. C
A brand name for indomethacin is Indocin.

44. A
Indomethacin is classified as an NSAID.

45. D
Among other conditions, indomethacin is indicated for the treatment of pain associated with acute gout. Indomethacin is not indicated for the treatment of pain associated with migraines, fibromyalgia, or muscle spasms.

46. B
A brand name for insulin aspart is Novolog.

47. B

Insulin aspart is a rapid-acting insulin.

48. D

A brand name for insulin detemir is Levemir FlexTouch.

49. A

Insulin detemir is a long-acting insulin.

50. C

Pens or vials of insulin detemir that are in use can be stored at room temperature for 42 days.

51. D

A brand name for insulin glargine is Lantus.

52. B

Insulin glargine is a long-acting insulin.

53. B

Insulin glargine is typically dosed once a day.

54. A

A brand name for regular human insulin is Novolin R.

55. C

Regular human insulin is a short-acting insulin.

56. A

Regular human insulin is typically dosed 30 minutes before a meal.

57. A

A brand name for insulin lispro is Humalog.

58. D

Insulin lispro is a rapid-acting insulin.

59. C

Patients should rotate injection sites when administering insulin, such as insulin lispro, to prevent lipohypertrophy.

60. B

A brand name for ipratropium is Atrovent HFA.

61. A

Ipratropium is classified as an anticholinergic.

62. C

Among other conditions, ipratropium is indicated for the treatment of COPD.

63. D
The brand name for irbesartan is Avapro.

64. B
Irbesartan is classified as an antihypertensive.

65. C
Patients receiving irbesartan should have their potassium levels monitored as it can cause hyperkalemia.

66. D
A brand name for isosorbide mononitrate is Imdur.

67. B
Isosorbide mononitrate is classified as an antianginal agent.

68. A
Immediate release isosorbide mononitrate is typically dosed 2 times daily with 7 hours between doses to avoid tolerance.

69. C
Isosorbide mononitrate should not be used concomitantly with PDE-5 inhibitors, such as tadalafil, due to the risk of symptomatic hypotension.

70. D
A brand name for ketoconazole is Nizoral.

71. B
Ketoconazole is classified as an antifungal.

72. A
In addition to other dosage forms, topical ketoconazole is available as a cream, shampoo, and foam. Topical ketoconazole is not available as a solution.

73. A
A brand name for labetalol is Trandate.

74. C
Labetalol is classified as an antihypertensive.

75. B
Labetalol blocks $alpha_1$-, $beta_1$-, and $beta_2$-receptors. Labetalol does not block $alpha_2$-receptors.

76. D
The brand name for lamotrigine is Lamictal.

77. A
Lamotrigine is classified as an anticonvulsant.

78. C
A titration schedule is often followed when initiating therapy with lamotrigine to reduce the risk of skin rashes.

79. B
Lamotrigine is available as an oral tablet.

80. D
The brand name for lansoprazole is Prevacid.

81. A
Lansoprazole is classified as a PPI.

82. D
Among other vitamins and minerals, lansoprazole can affect the absorption of calcium, vitamin B_{12}, and magnesium. Lansoprazole does not affect the absorption of vitamin A.

83. C
The highest strength that is available for lansoprazole oral capsules is 30 mg.

84. A
The brand name for latanoprost is Xalatan.

85. B
Latanoprost is classified as a prostaglandin analog.

86. D
Latanoprost is indicated for the treatment of glaucoma.

87. B
After opening, latanoprost may be stored at room temperature for 6 weeks.

88. C
The brand name for letrozole is Femara.

89. A
Letrozole is classified as an aromatase inhibitor.

90. C
Letrozole is indicated for the treatment of breast cancer in postmenopausal women.

91. D
The brand name for levalbuterol is Xopenex.

92. B
Levalbuterol is classified as a $beta_2$-agonist.

93. A
Levalbuterol is indicated for the treatment of asthma.

94. B
Among other adverse effects, levalbuterol may cause tremor, tachycardia, hyperglycemia, and cough.

95. D
A brand name for levetiracetam is Keppra.

96. A
Levetiracetam is classified as an anticonvulsant.

97. B
Immediate release levetiracetam tablets are typically dosed two times daily.

98. D
The brand name for levocetirizine is Xyzal.

99. C
Levocetrizine is classified as an H_1 antagonist.

100. B
Levocetirizine is available in 5 mg oral tablets.

101. D
A brand name for levofloxacin is Levaquin.

102. C
Levofloxacin is classified as an antibiotic.

103. D
Levofloxacin is available in 250 mg, 500 mg, and 750 mg oral tablets. Levofloxacin is not available in 1,000 mg oral tablets.

104. A
Among other medications, antacids can decrease the absorption of levofloxacin.

105. B
A brand name for levothyroxine is Levoxyl.

106. D
Levothyroxine is classified as a thyroid product.

107. D
Levothyroxine is synthetic T_4.

108. C
Among other adverse effects, a patient may experience tachycardia if their dose of levothyroxine is too high. Fatigue, cold intolerance, and weight gain are symptoms a patient may experience if their dose of levothyroxine is too low.

109. A
A brand name for topical lidocaine is Lidoderm.

110. B
Topical lidocaine is classified as an analgesic.

111. D
Lidocaine topical patches should be removed after 12 hours to prevent tolerance. No more than 3 patches should be applied at one time and the patches should not be covered with a heating pad or electric blanket. Lidocaine patches can be cut into smaller pieces.

112. A
Lidocaine topical patches should be used with caution when used concomitantly with class I antiarrhythmics due to additive and potentially synergistic toxic effects.

113. C
The brand name for linagliptan is Tradjenta.

114. D
Linagliptan is classified as a DPP-4 inhibitor.

115. B
Linagliptan is indicated for the treatment of diabetes.

116. A
Linagliptan is available in 5 mg oral tablets.

117. D
A brand name for liraglutide is Victoza.

118. B
Liraglutide is classified as a GLP-1 receptor agonist.

119. A
Liraglutide is available as a subcutaneous solution.

120. D
Liraglutide has a black box warning regarding the risk of thyroid C-cell tumors.

121. C
The brand name for lisdexamfetamine is Vyvanse.

122. D
Lisdexamfetamine is classified as a CNS stimulant.

123. B
Lisdexamfetamine is indicated for the treatment of ADHD, as well as binge eating disorder.

124. A
The maximum recommended daily dose for lisdexamfetamine is 70 mg.

125. A
A brand name for lisinopril is Prinivil.

126. C
Lisinopril is classified as an ACE inhibitor.

127. B
Among other adverse effects, lisinopril may cause dizziness, hyperkalemia, angioedema, and cough.

128. C
A brand name for lisinopril-hydrochlorothiazide is Zestoretic.

129. A
Lisinopril-hydrochlorothiazide is classified as an antihypertensive.

130. A
Lisinopril-hydrochlorothiazide is available as an oral tablet.

131. D
A brand name for lithium carbonate is Lithobid.

132. A
Lithium carbonate is classified as an antimanic agent.

133. C
Caffeine, increased salt intake, and theophylline can decrease lithium levels. NSAIDs can increase lithium levels.

134. B
The brand name for lorazepam is Ativan.

135. D
Lorazepam is classified as a benzodiazepine.

136. C
Among other conditions, lorazepam is indicated for the treatment of anxiety.

137. A
Lorazepam is available in 0.5 mg, 1 mg, and 2 mg oral tablets. Lorazepam is not available in 0.25 mg oral tablets.

138. B
The brand name for losartan is Cozaar.

139. A
Losartan is classified as an ARB.

140. D
Losartan should be avoided in women who are pregnant due to the risk of birth defects.

141. B
The brand name for losartan-hydrochlorothiazide is Hyzaar.

142. A
Losartan-hydrochlorothiazide is classified as an antihypertensive.

143. C
Losartan-hydrochlorothiazide is available as an oral tablet.

144. D
A brand name for loteprednol is Lotemax.

145. B
Loteprednol is classified as a corticosteroid.

146. A
Among other conditions, loteprednol is indicated for the treatment of allergic conjunctivitis.

147. D
A brand name for lovastatin is Mevacor.

148. A
Lovastatin is classified as an HMG-CoA reductase inhibitor.

149. C
Lovastatin is available in 10 mg, 20 mg, and 40 mg oral tablets. Lovastatin is not available in 30 mg oral tablets.

150. B
The brand name for lubiprostone is Amitiza.

151. D
Lubiprostone is classified as a chloride channel activator.

152. A
Among other indications, lubiprostone is indicated for the treatment of chronic idiopathic constipation.

153. A
Lubiprostone should be taken with food and water to decrease nausea.

154. C
The brand name for lurasidone is Latuda.

155. B
Lurasidone is classified as an antipsychotic.

156. D
Among other adverse effects, lurasidone may cause nausea, weight gain, akathisia, and hyperglycemia.

157. A
Lurasidone is available as an oral tablet.

DRUGS M – N

QUESTIONS

Meclizine

1. Which of the following is a brand name for meclizine?

a. Beyaz
b. Antivert
c. Lastacaft
d. Kenalog

2. Meclizine belongs to which of the following pharmacologic classes?

a. Antihistamine
b. Hypnotic
c. Antibiotic
d. Antianginal agent

3. Meclizine is available in which of the following dosage forms?

a. Transdermal patch
b. Ophthalmic solution
c. Oral tablet
d. Oral solution

4. Meclizine should be used with caution in patients with which of the following conditions?

a. Gout
b. Macular degeneration
c. Anemia
d. BPH

Medroxyprogesterone

5. Which of the following is a brand name for medroxyprogesterone?

a. Seasonique
b. Provera
c. Carafate
d. Eucrisa

6. Medroxyprogesterone belongs to which of the following pharmacologic classes?

a. Progestin
b. Gonadotropin
c. SERM
d. Prolactin inhibitor

7. Medroxyprogesterone is indicated for the treatment of all but which of the following conditions?

a. Endometriosis
b. Amenorrhea
c. Premature ovarian failure
d. Abnormal uterine bleeding

8. When being used for contraception, injectable medroxyprogesterone should be administered every _____ months.

a. two
b. three
c. four
d. six

Meloxicam

9. Which of the following is a brand name for meloxicam?

a. Bentyl
b. Tivorbex
c. Mobic
d. Quillivant XR

10. Meloxicam belongs to which of the following pharmacologic classes?

a. NSAID
b. Fibrate
c. Tricyclic antidepressant
d. PPI

11. Which of the following is the maximum daily dose for meloxicam oral tablets?

a. 10 mg
b. 15 mg
c. 20 mg
d. 30 mg

Memantine

12. Which of the following is the brand name for memantine?

a. Viibryd
b. Latisse
c. Harvoni
d. Namenda

13. Memantine belongs to which of the following pharmacologic classes?

a. CNS stimulant
b. NMDA receptor antagonist
c. Estrogen receptor antagonist
d. Cholinesterase inhibitor

14. Memantine is indicated for the treatment of which of the following conditions?

a. Osteoporosis
b. Depression
c. Alzheimer's disease
d. Rheumatoid arthritis

15. Memantine is available in all but which of the following dosage forms?

a. Transdermal patch
b. Oral capsule
c. Oral solution
d. Oral tablet

Mesalamine

16. Which of the following is a brand name for mesalamine?

a. Farxiga
b. Diflucan
c. Vicoprofen
d. Pentasa

17. Mesalamine belongs to which of the following pharmacologic classes?

a. Aminosalicylate
b. $5HT_3$ receptor antagonist
c. Aromatase inhibitor
d. Beta$_2$-agonist

18. Mesalamine is indicated for the treatment of which of the following conditions?

a. GERD
b. Overactive bladder
c. Ulcerative colitis
d. Parkinson's disease

19. Mesalamine is available in all but which of the following dosage forms?

a. Rectal enema
b. Oral capsule
c. Rectal suppository
d. Oral solution

Metaxalone

20. Which of the following is a brand name for metaxalone?

a. Voltaren
b. Skelaxin
c. Actiq
d. Trulance

21. Metaxalone belongs to which of the following pharmacologic classes?

a. Skeletal muscle relaxant
b. Anticonvulsant
c. Analgesic
d. Nasal decongestant

22. Metaxolone is available in which of the following dosage forms?

a. Topical gel
b. Intramuscular suspension
c. Oral tablet
d. Nasal spray

Metformin

23. Which of the following is a brand name for metformin?

a. Coreg
b. Fortaz
c. Colestid
d. Glucophage

24. Metformin belongs to which of the following pharmacologic classes?

a. GLP-1 agonist
b. Biguanide
c. Aldosterone receptor antagonist
d. H_2 receptor antagonist

25. Metformin has a black box warning regarding the risk of which of the following?

a. Pancreatitis
b. Stevens-Johnson syndrome
c. Lactic acidosis
d. GI perforation

26. Metformin can decrease the absorption of which of the following vitamins?

a. Vitamin A
b. Vitamin B_{12}
c. Vitamin C
d. Vitamin K

Metformin-glyburide

27. Which of the following is the brand name for metformin-glyburide?

a. Glynase
b. Prandimet
c. Glucovance
d. Fuzeon

28. Metformin-glyburide belongs to which of the following pharmacologic classes?

a. Antidiabetic
b. Immunosuppressant
c. Antihyperlipidemic
d. Antiasthma agent

29. Which of the following administration techniques applies to metformin-glyburide?

a. Avoid antacids.
b. Take with food.
c. Remain upright for 30 minutes.
d. Avoid grapefruit juice.

Methadone

30. Which of the following is a brand name for methadone?

a. Addyi
b. Lortab
c. Efudex
d. Dolophine

31. Methadone belongs to which of the following pharmacologic classes?

a. Opioid analgesic
b. ACE inhibitor
c. Protease inhibitor
d. Calcium channel blocker

32. Methadone has a black box warning regarding the risk of which of the following?

a. Thrombocytopenia
b. Exfoliative dermatitis
c. QT prolongation
d. Stomatitis

Methimazole

33. Which of the following is the brand name for methimazole?

a. Vasotec
b. Tapazole
c. Depacon
d. Accutane

34. Methimazole belongs to which of the following pharmacologic classes?

a. Antithyroid agent
b. Antidiabetic
c. Antipsychotic
d. Antihypertensive

35. Methimazole is available in which of the following dosage forms?

a. Oral solution
b. Subcutaneous solution
c. Nasal spray
d. Oral tablet

Methocarbamol

36. Which of the following is the brand name for methocarbamol?

a. Robaxin
b. Dovonex
c. Bactrim
d. Eligard

37. Methocarbamol belongs to which of the following pharmacologic classes?

a. Potassium-sparing diuretic
b. Inotropic agent
c. Skeletal muscle relaxant
d. COX-2 inhibitor

38. Methocarbamol may cause all but which of the following adverse effects?

a. Bradycardia
b. Hypotension
c. Drowsiness
d. Dizziness

Methotrexate

39. Which of the following is a brand name for methotrexate?

a. Restasis
b. Cartia XT
c. Erbitux
d. Trexall

40. Methotrexate belongs to which of the following pharmacologic classes?

a. Mast cell stabilizer
b. Antineoplastic agent
c. Vasopressor
d. Hematopoietic agent

41. Methotrexate may cause all but which of the following toxicities?

a. Cardiotoxicity
b. Renal toxicity
c. Hepatic toxicity
d. Pulmonary toxicity

42. Methotrexate is indicated for the treatment of all but which of the following conditions?

a. Rheumatoid arthritis
b. Psoriasis
c. Breast cancer
d. Cushing's syndrome

Methylphenidate

43. Which of the following is a brand name for methylphenidate?

a. Tessalon
b. Concerta
c. Actemra
d. Focalin

44. Methylphenidate belongs to which of the following pharmacologic classes?

a. Sedative
b. Antidepressant
c. CNS stimulant
d. Antianxiety agent

45. Methylphenidate is contraindicated in patients with which of the following conditions?

a. Tourette syndrome
b. Alzheimer's disease
c. Multiple sclerosis
d. Addison's disease

46. Methylphenidate is available in all but which of the following dosage forms?

a. Oral tablet
b. Transdermal patch
c. Oral capsule
d. Intramuscular suspension

Methylprednisolone

47. Which of the following is a brand name for methylprednisolone?

a. Medrol
b. Oscimin
c. Trilafon
d. Humira

48. Methylprednisolone belongs to which of the following pharmacologic classes?

a. Antiandrogen
b. Bronchodilator
c. Corticosteroid
d. Antibiotic

49. All but which of the following may be adverse effects of methylprednisolone?

a. Increased appetite
b. Edema
c. Insomnia
d. Hypoglycemia

50. A methylprednisolone dose-pack provides _____ days of therapy.

a. 3
b. 6
c. 10
d. 14

Metoclopramide

51. Which of the following is a brand name for metoclopramide?

a. Reglan
b. Altoprev
c. Pristiq
d. Xylocaine

52. Metoclopramide belongs to which of the following pharmacologic classes?

a. Urinary antispasmodic
b. Gastric antisecretory
c. Anticoagulant
d. Prokinetic agent

53. Metoclopramide is indicated for the treatment of all but which of the following conditions?

a. Diabetic gastroparesis
b. Chron's disease
c. GERD
d. Postoperative nausea and vomiting

54. Metoclopramide has a black box warning about the risk of which of the following adverse effects?

a. Serotonin syndrome
b. Ischemic colitis
c. Tardive dyskinesia
d. AV block

Metoprolol

55. Which of the following is a brand name for metoprolol?

a. Lopressor
b. Rebif
c. Aricept
d. Desferal

56. Metoprolol belongs to which of the following pharmacologic classes?

a. Analgesic
b. Antidiabetic
c. Antifungal
d. Antihypertensive

57. Metoprolol blocks which of the following receptors?

a. Alpha$_1$
b. Beta$_1$
c. Alpha$_1$ and beta$_1$
d. Beta$_1$ and beta$_2$

58. Metoprolol should be tapered when discontinuing chronic therapy to reduce the risk of which of the following?

a. Renal artery stenosis
b. Angioedema
c. Bronchospasm
d. Ischemic syndromes

Metronidazole

59. Which of the following is a brand name for metronidazole?

a. Flagyl
b. Imuran
c. Advicor
d. BenzaClin

60. Metronidazole belongs to which of the following pharmacologic classes?

a. Antitussive
b. Antianxiety agent
c. Antibiotic
d. Antiemetic

61. Patients taking metronidazole should avoid which of the following?

a. Dairy products
b. Alcohol
c. Leafy greens
d. Grapefruit

62. Metronidazole is available in all but which of the following dosage forms?

a. Ophthalmic suspension
b. Topical cream
c. Oral tablet
d. Vaginal gel

Minocycline

63. Which of the following is a brand name for minocycline?

a. Tekturna HCT
b. Levemir
c. Eskalith
d. Solodyn

64. Minocycline belongs to which of the following pharmacologic classes?

a. Hypnotic
b. Antibiotic
c. Antihypertensive
d. NSAID

65. Minocycline should be avoided in which of the following patient populations?

a. Patients with hepatic impairment
b. Patients over 65 years of age with anemia
c. Children 8 years of age and younger
d. Patients with a sulfa allergy

66. The absorption of minocycline can be decreased by all but which of the following?

a. Vitamin K
b. Iron
c. Calcium
d. Aluminum

Mirtazapine

67. Which of the following is the brand name for mirtazapine?

a. Remeron
b. Intuniv
c. Betimol
d. Amrix

68. Mirtazapine belongs to which of the following pharmacologic classes?

a. Antipsychotic
b. Antiparkinson agent
c. GI antisecretory
d. Antidepressant

69. All but which of the following may be adverse effects of mirtazapine?

a. Weight gain
b. Sialorrhea
c. Drowsiness
d. Increased appetite

Modafinil

70. Which of the following is the brand name for modafinil?

a. Teflaro
b. Cordarone
c. Provigil
d. Fiorinol

71. Modafinil belongs to which of the following pharmacologic classes?

a. CNS stimulant
b. Phosphate binder
c. Sedative
d. Antidiarrheal

72. Modafinil belongs to which of the following DEA Schedules?

a. Schedule II
b. Schedule III
c. Schedule IV
d. Schedule V

73. Modafinil is indicated for the treatment of all but which of the following conditions?

a. Narcolepsy
b. Shift-work sleep disorder
c. Obstructive sleep apnea
d. Jet lag

Mometasone

74. Which of the following is a brand name for mometasone?

a. Soriatane
b. Nasonex
c. Fortesta
d. Avodart

75. Mometasone belongs to which of the following pharmacologic classes?

a. H_2 receptor antagonist
b. Anticholinergic
c. Corticosteroid
d. Alpha$_1$-agonist

76. Which of the following is the most appropriate dosing of mometasone when used for allergic rhinitis?

a. Two sprays in each nostril once daily
b. Two sprays in each nostril twice daily
c. Two sprays in each nostril three times daily
d. Two sprays in each nostril four times daily

Mometasone-formoterol

77. Which of the following is the brand name for mometasone-formoterol?

a. Flomax
b. Marinol
c. Serax
d. Dulera

78. Mometasone-formoterol belongs to which of the following pharmacologic classes?

a. Antianginal
b. Antiasthma agent
c. Antihistamine
d. Antiplatelet agent

79. Mometasone-formoterol is available in which of the following dosage forms?

a. Inhalation aerosol
b. Nebulizer solution
c. Nasal spray
d. Oral solution

Montelukast

80. Which of the following is the brand name for montelukast?

a. Taclonex
b. Adderall
c. Singulair
d. Norflex

81. Montelukast belongs to which of the following pharmacologic classes?

a. SSRI
b. Leukotriene receptor antagonist
c. Beta-agonist
d. Benzodiazepine

82. Montelukast is indicated for the treatment of which of the following conditions?

a. Asthma
b. IBS
c. Insomnia
d. Alzheimer's disease

83. Montelukast is available in all but which of the following oral tablet strengths?

a. 4 mg
b. 5 mg
c. 10 mg
d. 12 mg

Morphine

84. Which of the following is a brand name for morphine?

a. Tarceva
b. MS Contin
c. Nucynta ER
d. Macrodantin

85. Morphine belongs to which of the following pharmacologic classes?

a. Opioid analgesic
b. Anticonvulsant
c. Antiemetic
d. Skeletal muscle relaxant

86. Tolerance usually develops to all but which of the following adverse effects of morphine?

a. Sedation
b. Nausea
c. Constipation
d. Respiratory depression

Moxifloxacin

87. Which of the following is a brand name for moxifloxacin?

a. Novolog
b. Stelara
c. Trilyte
d. Avelox

88. Moxifloxacin belongs to which of the following pharmacologic classes?

a. Fluoroquinolone antibiotic
b. Cephalosporin antibiotic
c. Macrolide antibiotic
d. Tetracycline antibiotic

89. Moxifloxacin is available in which of the following oral tablet strengths?

a. 200 mg
b. 400 mg
c. 500 mg
d. 750 mg

Mupirocin

90. Which of the following is a brand name for mupirocin?

a. Lotrel
b. Silvadene
c. Eldepryl
d. Bactroban

91. Mupirocin belongs to which of the following pharmacologic classes?

a. Corticosteroid
b. Analgesic
c. Antibiotic
d. Antiviral

92. Mupirocin is available in which of the following dosage forms?

a. Topical ointment
b. Oral tablet
c. Topical solution
d. Nasal spray

Mycophenolate mofetil

93. Which of the following is a brand name for mycophenolate mofetil?

a. Neoral
b. Microzide
c. CellCept
d. Testim

94. Mycophenolate mofetil belongs to which of the following pharmacologic classes?

a. Antihyperlipidemic
b. Immunosuppressant
c. Antineoplastic agent
d. Hematopoietic agent

95. Mycophenolate mofetil is indicated for the prevention or treatment of which of the following conditions?

a. Systemic lupus erythematosus
b. Rheumatoid arthritis
c. Multiple sclerosis
d. Organ transplant rejection

Nabumetone

96. Which of the following is the brand name for nabumetone?

a. Relafen
b. Desonate
c. Thorazine
d. Femhrt

97. Nabumetone belongs to which of the following pharmacologic classes?

a. Potassium supplement
b. Statin
c. NSAID
d. Bronchodilator

98. Nabumetone is indicated for the treatment of which of the following conditions?

a. Migraine
b. Arthritis
c. Gout
d. Fever

99. Which of the following is the maximum daily dose for nabumetone?

a. 1,000 mg
b. 2,000 mg
c. 3,000 mg
d. 4,000 mg

Naproxen

100. Which of the following is a brand name for naproxen?

a. Vectical
b. Nexium
c. Tiazac
d. Naprosyn

101. Naproxen belongs to which of the following pharmacologic classes?

a. Aromatase inhibitor
b. PPI
c. NSAID
d. Incretin mimetic

102. Naproxen is indicated for the treatment of all but which of the following conditions?

a. Fibromyalgia
b. Dysmenorrhea
c. Acute gout
d. Osteoarthritis

Nebivolol

103. Which of the following is the brand name for nebivolol?

a. Cortef
b. Bystolic
c. Lodine
d. Mydayis

104. Nebivolol belongs to which of the following pharmacologic classes?

a. HMG -CoA reductase inhibitor
b. Sulfonylurea
c. Potassium sparing diuretic
d. Beta-blocker

105. Nebivolol is indicated for the treatment of which of the following conditions?

a. Hypertension
b. Allergic rhinitis
c. Angina
d. Restless legs syndrome

Neomycin-polymixin B-hydrocortisone

106. Which of the following is a brand name for neomycin-polymixin B-hydrocortisone?

a. Silenor
b. Epiduo
c. Cortisporin
d. Vigamox

107. Neomycin-polymixin B-hydrocortisone is a combination of which of the following classes of medications?

a. Antibiotic and NSAID
b. Antifungal and corticosteroid
c. Antifungal and keratolytic agent
d. Antibiotic and corticosteroid

108. Neomycin-polymixin B-hydrocortisone is available in all but which of the following dosage forms?

a. Topical solution
b. Otic solution
c. Ophthalmic suspension
d. Topical cream

Niacin

109. Which of the following is a brand name for niacin?

a. Ilevro
b. Estrace
c. Cymbalta
d. Niaspan

110. Niacin belongs to which of the following pharmacologic classes?

a. Antidiabetic
b. Antihyperlipidemic
c. Antigout agent
d. Antihypertensive

111. Which of the following administration techniques can minimize flushing caused by niacin?

a. Take with food.
b. Take with a hot beverage.
c. Take aspirin or an NSAID at the same time as niacin.
d. Take with milk.

112. Niacin may cause all but which of the following adverse effects?

a. Gout
b. Hepatoxicity
c. Hypertension
d. GI distress

Nifedipine

113. Which of the following is a brand name for nifedipine?

a. Lysteda
b. Procardia
c. Lexapro
d. Calan

114. Nifedipine belongs to which of the following pharmacologic classes?

a. H_2 receptor antagonist
b. Thiazolidinedione
c. Protease inhibitor
d. Calcium channel blocker

115. Nifedipine is indicated for the treatment of which of the following conditions?

a. Hypertension
b. BPH
c. Anxiety
d. COPD

116. Nifedipine may cause which of the following adverse effects?

a. Dry mouth
b. Lupus-like syndrome
c. Peripheral edema
d. Hyperkalemia

Nitrofurantoin

117. Which of the following is a brand name for nitrofurantoin?

a. Zaroxolyn
b. Macrobid
c. Spritam
d. Augmentin

118. Nitrofurantoin belongs to which of the following pharmacologic classes?

a. Antibiotic
b. GI stimulant
c. Antifungal
d. Antidiarrheal

119. Which of the following administration techniques applies to nitrofurantoin?

a. Do not take concomitantly with calcium products.
b. Remain upright for 30 minutes after taking.
c. Avoid alcohol.
d. Take with food.

120. Nitrofurantoin may cause which of the following adverse effects when used long term?

a. Pulmonary fibrosis
b. Gingival hyperplasia
c. Rhabdomyolysis
d. Osteoporosis

Nitroglycerin

121. Which of the following is a brand name for nitroglycerin?

a. Zetia
b. Avage
c. Nitrostat
d. Kaletra

122. Nitroglycerin belongs to which of the following pharmacologic classes?

a. Anticoagulant
b. Antianginal agent
c. Anticonvulsant
d. Antigout agent

123. Nitroglycerin is available in all but which of the following dosage forms?

a. Transdermal patch
b. Topical ointment
c. Sublingual spray
d. Nasal spray

124. Which of the following statements applies to sublingual nitroglycerin tablets?

a. The tablets can be crushed.
b. Store the tablets in the original amber glass container.
c. The tablets expire 6 months after opening the amber glass container.
d. The tablets can be taken at 2 minute intervals.

Norethindrone

125. Which of the following is a brand name for norethindrone?

a. Ortho Micronor
b. Mitigare
c. Levora
d. Azasan

126. Norethindrone belongs to which of the following pharmacologic classes?

a. Estrogen receptor antagonist
b. Antigonadotropic agent
c. Oral contraceptive
d. Antidiuretic hormone

Nortriptyline

127. Which of the following is a brand name for nortriptyline?

a. Uloric
b. Pamelor
c. Deplin
d. Simbrinza

128. Nortriptyline belongs to which of the following pharmacologic classes?

a. Monoclonal antibody
b. Antianxiety agent
c. Antiplatelet agent
d. Tricyclic antidepressant

129. Nortriptyline is contraindicated with the concomitant use of which of the following classes of medications?

a. PDE-5 inhibitors
b. PPIs
c. MAO inhibitors
d. Factor Xa inhibitors

Nystatin

130. Which of the following is a brand name for nystatin?

a. Nyamyc
b. Periogard
c. Neupro
d. Mirvaso

131. Nystatin belongs to which of the following pharmacologic classes?

a. Keratolytic
b. Antihistamine
c. Antifungal
d. Corticosteroid

132. Nystatin is available in all but which of the following dosage forms?

a. Topical cream
b. Shampoo
c. Topical powder
d. Oral suspension

ANSWER KEY

1. B
A brand name for meclizine is Antivert.

2. A
Meclizine is classified as an antihistamine.

3. C
Meclizine is available as an oral tablet.

4. D
Among other conditions, meclizine should be used with caution in patients with BPH because it will worsen BPH symptoms and make it more difficult to urinate.

5. B
A brand name for medroxyprogesterone is Provera.

6. A
Medroxyprogesterone is classified as a progestin.

7. C
Among other indications, medroxyprogesterone is indicated for the treatment of endometriosis, amenorrhea, and abnormal uterine bleeding. Medroxyprogesterone is not indicated for the treatment of premature ovarian failure.

8. B
When being used for contraception, injectable medroxyprogesterone should be administered every three months.

9. C
A brand name for meloxicam is Mobic.

10. A
Meloxicam is classified as an NSAID.

11. B
The maximum daily dose for meloxicam oral tablets is 15 mg.

12. D
The brand name for memantine is Namenda.

13. B
Memantine is classified as an NMDA receptor antagonist.

14. C
Memantine is indicated for the treatment of Alzheimer's disease.

15. A
Memantine is available as an oral capsule, oral solution, and oral tablet. Memantine is not available as a transdermal patch.

16. D
A brand name for mesalamine is Pentasa.

17. A
Mesalamine is classified as an aminosalicylate.

18. C
Among other conditions, mesalamine is indicated for the treatment of ulcerative colitis.

19. D
Among other dosage forms, mesalamine is available as a rectal enema, oral capsule, and rectal suppository. Mesalamine is not available as an oral solution.

20. B
A brand name for metaxalone is Skelaxin.

21. A
Metaxalone is classified as a skeletal muscle relaxant.

22. C
Metaxolone is available as an oral tablet.

23. D
A brand name for metformin is Glucophage.

24. B
Metformin is classified as a biguanide.

25. C
Metformin has a black box warning regarding the risk of lactic acidosis.

26. B
Metformin can decrease the absorption of vitamin B_{12}.

27. C
The brand name for metformin-glyburide is Glucovance.

28. A
Metformin-glyburide is classified as an antidiabetic.

29. B
Metformin-glyburide should be taken with food to decrease GI upset.

30. D
A brand name for methadone is Dolophine.

31. A
Methadone is classified as an opioid analgesic.

32. C
Methadone has a black box warning regarding the risk of QT prolongation.

33. B
The brand name for methimazole is Tapazole.

34. A
Methimazole is classified as an antithyroid agent.

35. D
Methimazole is available as an oral tablet.

36. A
The brand name for methocarbamol is Robaxin.

37. C
Methocarbamol is classified as a skeletal muscle relaxant.

38. B
Among other adverse effects, methocarbamol may cause bradycardia, hypertension, drowsiness, and dizziness.

39. D
A brand name for methotrexate is Trexall.

40. B
Methotrexate is classified as an antineoplastic agent.

41. A
Methotrexate may cause renal, hepatic, and pulmonary toxicity. Methotrexate is not associated with cardiotoxicity.

42. D
Among other conditions, methotrexate is indicated for the treatment of rheumatoid arthritis, psoriasis, and breast cancer. Methotrexate is not indicated for the treatment of Cushing's syndrome.

43. B
A brand name for methylphenidate is Concerta.

44. C
Methylphenidate is classified as a CNS stimulant.

45. A
Methylphenidate is contraindicated in patients with Tourette syndrome, or a family history of Tourette syndrome due to the risk of tics.

46. D
Methylphenidate is available as an oral tablet, transdermal patch, and oral capsule. Methylphenidate is not available as an intramuscular suspension.

47. A
A brand name for methylprednisolone is Medrol.

48. C
Methylprednisolone is classified as a corticosteroid.

49. D
Among other adverse effects, methylprednisolone may cause increased appetite, edema, insomnia, and hyperglycemia.

50. B
A methylprednisolone dose-pack provides 6 days of therapy.

51. A
A brand name for metoclopramide is Reglan.

52. D
Metoclopramide is classified as a prokinetic agent.

53. B
Among other indications, metoclopramide is indicated for the treatment of diabetic gastroparesis, GERD, and postoperative nausea and vomiting. Metoclopramide is not indicated for the treatment of Chron's disease.

54. C
Metoclopramide has a black box warning about the risk of tardive dyskinesia.

55. A
A brand name for metoprolol is Lopressor.

56. D
Metoprolol is classified as an antihypertensive.

57. B
Metoprolol blocks beta$_1$-receptors.

58. D
Metoprolol should be tapered when discontinuing chronic therapy to reduce the risk of ischemic syndromes, such as exacerbation of angina and myocardial infarction.

59. A
A brand name for metronidazole is Flagyl.

60. C
Metronidazole is classified as an antibiotic.

61. B
Patients taking metronidazole should avoid alcohol due to a disulfiram-like reaction.

62. A
Among other dosage forms, metronidazole is available as a topical cream, oral tablet, and vaginal gel. Metronidazole is not available as an ophthalmic suspension.

63. D
A brand name for minocycline is Solodyn.

64. B
Minocycline is classified as an antibiotic.

65. C
Minocycline is a tetracycline and should therefore be avoided in children 8 years of age and younger due to the risk of causing permanent tooth discoloration.

66. A
Among other substances, the absorption of minocycline can be decreased by iron, calcium, and aluminum. The absorption of minocycline is not affected by vitamin K.

67. A
The brand name for mirtazapine is Remeron.

68. D
Mirtazapine is classified as an antidepressant.

69. B
In addition to other adverse effects, mirtazapine may cause weight gain, dry mouth, drowsiness, and increased appetite.

70. C
The brand name for modafinil is Provigil.

71. A
Modafinil is classified as a CNS stimulant.

72. C
Modafinil belongs to DEA Schedule IV.

73. D
Modafinil is indicated for the treatment of narcolepsy, shift-work sleep disorder, and obstructive sleep apnea. Modafinil is not indicated for the treatment of jet lag.

74. B
A brand name for mometasone is Nasonex.

75. C
Mometasone is classified as a corticosteroid.

76. A
The most appropriate dosing of mometasone when used for allergic rhinitis is two sprays in each nostril once daily.

77. D
The brand name for mometasone-formoterol is Dulera.

78. B
Mometasone-formoterol is classified as an antiasthma agent.

79. A
Mometasone-formoterol is available as an inhalation aerosol.

80. C
The brand name for montelukast is Singulair.

81. B
Montelukast is classified as a leukotriene receptor antagonist.

82. A
Montelukast is indicated for the treatment of asthma.

83. D
Montelukast is available in 4 mg, 5 mg, and 10 mg oral tablets. Montelukast is not available in 12 mg oral tablets.

84. B
A brand name for morphine is MS Contin.

85. A
Morphine is classified as an opioid analgesic.

86. C
Tolerance usually develops for some of the adverse effects of morphine, such as sedation, nausea, and respiratory depression. Tolerance to constipation caused by opioid analgesics generally does not occur.

87. D
A brand name for moxifloxacin is Avelox.

88. A
Moxifloxacin is classified as a fluoroquinolone antibiotic.

89. B
Moxifloxacin is available in 400 mg oral tablets.

90. D
A brand name for mupirocin is Bactroban.

91. C
Mupirocin is classified as an antibiotic.

92. A
Mupirocin is available as a topical ointment, as well as a topical cream.

93. C
A brand name for mycophenolate mofetil is CellCept.

94. B
Mycophenolate mofetil is classified as an immunosuppressant.

95. D
Mycophenolate mofetil is indicated for the prevention or treatment of organ transplant rejection.

96. A
The brand name for nabumetone is Relafen.

97. C
Nabumetone is classified as an NSAID.

98. B
Nabumetone is indicated for the treatment of arthritis (rheumatoid arthritis and osteoarthritis).

99. B
The maximum daily dose for nabumetone is 2,000 mg.

100. D
A brand name for naproxen is Naprosyn.

101. C
Naproxen is classified as an NSAID.

102. A
Among other indications, naproxen is indicated for the treatment of primary dysmenorrhea, acute gout, and osteoarthritis. Naproxen is not indicated for the treatment of fibromyalgia.

103. B
The brand name for nebivolol is Bystolic.

104. D
Nebivolol is classified as a beta-blocker.

105. A
Nebivolol is indicated for the treatment of hypertension.

106. C
A brand name for neomycin-polymixin B-hydrocortisone is Cortisporin.

107. D
Neomycin-polymixin B-hydrocortisone is a combination of an antibiotic and corticosteroid.

108. A
Among other dosage forms, neomycin-polymixin B-hydrocortisone is available as an otic solution, ophthalmic suspension, and topical cream. Neomycin-polymixin B-hydrocortisone is not available as a topical solution.

109. D
A brand name for niacin is Niaspan.

110. B
Niacin is classified as an antihyperlipidemic.

111. A
Taking niacin with food can minimize flushing caused by niacin. Avoiding hot beverages and taking aspirin or an NSAID 30 minutes prior to taking niacin can also minimize flushing. Taking niacin with milk does not minimize flushing.

112. C
Among other adverse effects, niacin may cause gout, hepatoxicity, hypotension, and GI distress.

113. B
A brand name for nifedipine is Procardia.

114. D
Nifedipine is classified as a calcium channel blocker.

115. A
Nifedipine is indicated for the treatment of hypertension, as well as chronic stable angina and variant angina.

116. C
Among other adverse effects, nifedipine may cause peripheral edema.

117. B
A brand name for nitrofurantoin is Macrobid.

118. A
Nitrofurantoin is classified as an antibiotic.

119. D
Nitrofurantoin should be taken with food to enhance absorption and decrease adverse effects.

120. A
Nitrofurantoin may cause pulmonary fibrosis when used long term.

121. C
A brand name for nitroglycerin is Nitrostat.

122. B
Nitroglycerin is classified as an antianginal agent.

123. D
Among other dosage forms, nitroglycerin is available as a transdermal patch, topical ointment, and sublingual spray. Nitroglycerin is not available as a nasal spray.

124. B
Sublingual nitroglycerin tablets should be stored in the original glass container and expire by the expiration date printed on the bottle by the manufacturer. The tablets cannot be crushed and should be placed under the tongue or in the buccal pouch to dissolve. The tablets can be taken at 5 minute intervals, up to 3 doses.

125. A
A brand name for norethindrone is Ortho Micronor.

126. C
Norethindrone is classified as an oral contraceptive.

127. B
A brand name for nortriptyline is Pamelor.

128. D
Nortriptyline is classified as a tricyclic antidepressant.

129. C
Nortriptyline is contraindicated with the concomitant use of MAO inhibitors or within 14 days of discontinuing an MAO inhibitor due to the risk of serotonin syndrome.

130. A
A brand name for nystatin is Nyamyc.

131. C
Nystatin is classified as an antifungal.

132. B
In addition to other dosage forms, nystatin is available as a topical cream, topical powder, and oral suspension. Nystatin is not available as a shampoo.

DRUGS O – R

QUESTIONS

Ofloxacin

1. Which of the following is a brand name for ofloxacin?

a. Ocuflox
b. Zorvolex
c. Alphagan P
d. Ocufen

2. Ofloxacin belongs to which of the following pharmacologic classes?

a. Penicillin antibiotic
b. Sulfonamide antibiotic
c. Macrolide antibiotic
d. Fluoroquinolone antibiotic

3. Ofloxacin is available in all but which of the following dosage forms?

a. Ophthalmic solution
b. Oral tablet
c. Topical gel
d. Otic solution

Olanzapine

4. Which of the following is the brand name for olanzapine?

a. Zyprexa
b. Valium
c. Fetzima
d. Uceris

5. Olanzapine belongs to which of the following pharmacologic classes?

a. Antihypertensive
b. Antipsychotic
c. Thrombolytic
d. Analgesic

6. All but which of the following should be monitored in patients taking olanzapine?

a. Blood pressure
b. Weight
c. Lipids
d. Liver enzymes

Olmesartan

7. Which of the following is the brand name for olmesartan?

a. Zyloprim
b. Wellbutrin
c. Benicar
d. Onfi

8. Olmesartan belongs to which of the following pharmacologic classes?

a. ARB
b. Diuretic
c. Statin
d. Biguanide

9. Olmesartan may cause which of the following electrolyte abnormalities?

a. Hypomagnesemia
b. Hyperkalemia
c. Hypercalcemia
d. Hyponatremia

Olmesartan-hydrochlorothiazide

10. Which of the following is the brand name for olmesartan-hydrochlorothiazide?

a. DuoNeb
b. Entresto
c. Aldactazide
d. Benicar HCT

11. Olmesartan-hydrochlorothiazide belongs to which of the following pharmacologic classes?

a. Antihypertensive
b. Antihyperlipidemic
c. Antigout agent
d. Antidepressant

12. Olmesartan-hydrochlorothiazide is available in which of the following dosage forms?

a. Oral capsule
b. Sublingual tablet
c. Oral tablet
d. Oral solution

Olopatadine

13. Which of the following is a brand name for olopatadine?

a. Cosopt
b. Patanase
c. Sitavig
d. Ovide

14. Olopatadine belongs to which of the following pharmacologic classes?

a. Antigluacoma agent
b. Calcineurin inhibitor
c. Endocrine agent
d. Antihistamine

15. Which of the following is the most appropriate dosing for olopatadine nasal spray?

a. One spray in each nostril once daily
b. Two sprays in each nostril once daily
c. Two sprays in each nostril twice daily
d. Two sprays in each nostril three times daily

Omega-3-acid ethyl esters

16. Which of the following is a brand name for omega-3-acid ethyl esters?

a. Lovaza
b. Invokana
c. Nesina
d. Clobex

17. Omega-3-acid ethyl esters belong to which of the following pharmacologic classes?

a. Antianginal agent
b. Antihyperlipidemic
c. Antihypertensive
d. Vasodilator

18. Omega-3-acid ethyl esters may cause all but which of the following adverse effects?

a. Dysguesia
b. Nausea
c. Diarrhea
d. Rhabdomyolysis

19. Omega-3-acid ethyl esters should be used with caution when used concomitantly with which of the following classes of medication?

a. Anticoagulants
b. Opioid analgesics
c. PPIs
d. Beta-blockers

Omeprazole

20. Which of the following is the brand name for omeprazole?

a. Myrbetriq
b. Omnicef
c. Prilosec
d. Lanoxin

21. Omeprazole belongs to which of the following pharmacologic classes?

a. SSRI
b. Alpha-agonist
c. Bile acid sequestrant
d. PPI

22. Omeprazole is available in all but which of the following oral capsule strengths?

a. 10 mg
b. 20 mg
c. 30 mg
d. 40 mg

23. Omeprazole may cause which of the following adverse effects when used long term?

a. Osteoporosis
b. Endocarditis
c. Gout
d. Diabetes

Ondansetron

24. Which of the following is a brand name for ondansetron?

a. Rosadan
b. Zofran
c. Celebrex
d. Veltin

25. Ondansetron belongs to which of the following pharmacologic classes?

a. PDE-4 inhibitor
b. Sulfonylurea
c. H_2 receptor antagonist
d. 5-HT_3 receptor antagonist

26. Ondansetron is indicated for the prevention of which of the following?

a. Nausea and vomiting
b. Angina
c. Migraine
d. Diarrhea

27. Ondansetron is available in which of the following oral tablet strengths?

a. 2 mg
b. 4 mg
c. 10 mg
d. 12 mg

Oseltamivir

28. Which of the following is the brand name for oseltamivir?

a. Pennsaid
b. Tamiflu
c. Zmax
d. Solaraze

29. Oseltamivir belongs to which of the following pharmacologic classes?

a. Antiemetic
b. Antibiotic
c. Antidiarrheal
d. Antiviral

30. Which of the following is the correct dosing regimen for oseltamivir for the treatment of influenza in adults with normal renal function?

a. 75 mg once daily for 5 days
b. 75 mg once daily for 10 days
c. 75 mg twice daily for 5 days
d. 75 mg three times daily for 5 days

31. Treatment with oseltamivir should be initiated within _____ hours of symptom onset.

a. 24
b. 48
c. 72
d. 96

Oxcarbazepine

32. Which of the following is a brand name for oxcarbazepine?

a. Biaxin
b. Zenzedi
c. Entocort EC
d. Trileptal

33. Oxcarbazepine belongs to which of the following pharmacologic classes?

a. Anticonvulsant
b. CNS stimulant
c. Analgesic
d. Sedative

34. Oxcarbazepine may cause which of the following electrolyte abnormalities?

a. Hypercalcemia
b. Hypochloremia
c. Hyponatremia
d. Hyperkalemia

Oxybutynin

35. Which of the following is a brand name for oxybutynin?

a. Gablofen
b. Ditropan XL
c. Astelin
d. Sinemet

36. Oxybutynin belongs to which of the following pharmacologic classes?

a. Laxative
b. Antiplatelet agent
c. Immunosuppressant
d. Urinary antispasmodic

37. Oxybutynin is available in all but which of the following dosage forms?

a. Oral capsule
b. Transdermal patch
c. Oral tablet
d. Topical gel

Oxycodone

38. Which of the following is a brand name for oxycodone?

a. BuSpar
b. MS Contin
c. OxyContin
d. Khedezla

39. Oxycodone belongs to which of the following pharmacologic classes?

a. Antianxiety agent
b. Opioid analgesic
c. Skeletal muscle relaxant
d. CNS stimulant

40. The levels of oxycodone can be increased by medications that inhibit which of the following enzymes?

a. CYP2C19
b. CYP3A4
c. CYP2D6
d. CYP2E1

Pantoprazole

41. Which of the following is the brand name for pantoprazole?

a. Haldol
b. Verelan
c. Protonix
d. Rocaltrol

42. Pantoprazole belongs to which of the following pharmacologic classes?

a. Tricyclic antidepressant
b. PPI
c. ACE inhibitor
d. Benzodiazepine

43. Pantoprazole can increase the risk of which of the following?

a. Pulmonary fibrosis
b. Gall stones
c. Hypertriglyceridemia
d. *C. difficile* infection

Paroxetine

44. Which of the following is a brand name for paroxetine?

a. Paxil
b. Jantoven
c. Relenza
d. Danocrine

45. Paroxetine belongs to which of the following pharmacologic classes?

a. Aminosalicylate
b. Statin
c. SSRI
d. Loop diuretic

46. Paroxetine is indicated for the treatment of all but which of the following conditions?

a. Major depressive disorder
b. Binge eating disorder
c. Social anxiety disorder
d. Panic disorder

Penicillin

47. Which of the following is a brand name for penicillin?

a. Jadenu
b. Cubicin
c. Keflex
d. Veetids

48. Penicillin belongs to which of the following pharmacologic classes?

a. Antiviral
b. Antitussive
c. Antibiotic
d. Anaphylaxis agent

49. Which of the following administration techniques applies to penicillin V potassium?

a. Take on an empty stomach.
b. Take with at least 8 oz. of water.
c. Take with a high fat meal.
d. Avoid grapefruit juice.

Phentermine

50. Which of the following is a brand name for phentermine?

a. Iressa
b. Adipex-P
c. Suprane
d. Ultracet

51. Phentermine belongs to which of the following pharmacologic classes?

a. Anticonvulsant
b. Opioid analgesic
c. Antiarrhythmic agent
d. Anorexiant

52. Phentermine should be avoided in patients with which of the following conditions?

a. Hypertension
b. Asthma
c. Hypothyroidism
d. Osteoporosis

53. Phentermine belongs to which of the following DEA Schedules?

a. Schedule II
b. Schedule III
c. Schedule IV
d. Schedule V

Phenytoin

54. Which of the following is a brand name for phenytoin?

a. Mobic
b. Dilantin
c. Epaned
d. Acuvail

55. Phenytoin belongs to which of the following pharmacologic classes?

a. Anticonvulsant
b. Antiparkinson agent
c. Antidepressant
d. Antihypertensive

56. Which of the following is the correct therapeutic range for phenytoin?

a. 10-20 mcg/L
b. 10-20 mg/mL
c. 10-20 mg/L
d. 10-20 mg/dL

57. Patients taking phenytoin long term may need supplementation with all but which of the following?

a. Calcium
b. Folic acid
c. Vitamin D
d. Iron

Pioglitazone

58. Which of the following is the brand name for pioglitazone?

a. Namzaric
b. Actos
c. Diovan
d. Adagen

59. Pioglitazone belongs to which of the following pharmacologic classes?

a. Thiazolidinedione
b. Calcium channel blocker
c. Benzodiazepine
d. PPI

60. Pioglitazone is indicated for the treatment of which of the following conditions?

a. Overactive bladder
b. Angina
c. Diabetes
d. Hypertension

61. Pioglitazone should be used with caution in patients with which of the following conditions?

a. Gout
b. Epilepsy
c. GERD
d. Congestive heart failure

Polyethylene glycol

62. Which of the following is a brand name for polyethylene glycol?

a. Inflectra
b. Miralax
c. Entereg
d. Reglan

63. Polyethylene glycol is classified as a/an _____ laxative.

a. osmotic
b. saline
c. stimulant
d. lubricant

Potassium chloride

64. Which of the following is a brand name for potassium chloride?

a. Urocit-K
b. Renagel
c. Klor-Con
d. Ceftin

65. Which of the following administration techniques applies to potassium chloride?

a. Do not take at the same time as antacids.
b. Take with food.
c. Avoid leafy greens.
d. Avoid hot beverages.

Pramipexole

66. Which of the following is the brand name for pramipexole?

a. Akten
b. Zubsolv
c. Proscar
d. Mirapex

67. Pramipexole belongs to which of the following pharmacologic classes?

a. Dopamine agonist
b. CNS stimulant
c. Renin inhibitor
d. Alpha$_2$-blocker

68. Pramipexole is indicated for the treatment of which of the following conditions?

a. Diabetes
b. Erectile dysfunction
c. Allergic conjunctivitis
d. Parkinson's disease

69. Pramipexole is available in which of the following dosage forms?

a. Oral solution
b. Ophthalmic solution
c. Oral tablet
d. Topical cream

Prasugrel

70. Which of the following is the brand name for prasugrel?

a. Effient
b. Imitrex
c. Xeljanz
d. Cutivate

71. Prasugrel belongs to which of the following pharmacologic classes?

a. Antihyperlipidemic
b. Antibiotic
c. Corticosteroid
d. Antiplatelet agent

72. Prasugrel is available in which of the following oral tablet strengths?

a. 10 mg
b. 20 mg
c. 30 mg
d. 40 mg

Pravastatin

73. Which of the following is the brand name for pravastatin?

a. Zocor
b. Janumet
c. Pravachol
d. Betagan

74. Pravastatin belongs to which of the following pharmacologic classes?

a. Potassium-sparing diuretic
b. HMG-CoA reductase inhibitor
c. 5-HT$_3$ receptor antagonist
d. COX-2 inhibitor

75. Pravastatin is contraindicated in which of the following conditions?

a. Hyperthyroidism
b. Multiple sclerosis
c. Rheumatoid arthritis
d. Pregnancy

Prednisolone

76. Which of the following is a brand name for prednisolone?

a. Millipred
b. Daxbia
c. Aldactone
d. Safyral

77. Prednisolone belongs to which of the following pharmacologic classes?

a. Antiviral
b. Analgesic
c. Corticosteroid
d. Sedative

78. Prednisolone is available in all but which of the following dosage forms?

a. Oral solution
b. Topical ointment
c. Ophthalmic suspension
d. Oral tablet

Prednisone

79. Which of the following is a brand name for prednisone?

a. Comtan
b. Vesicare
c. Deltasone
d. Bravelle

80. Prednisone belongs to which of the following pharmacologic classes?

a. Statin
b. Skeletal muscle relaxant
c. Cholinesterase inhibitor
d. Corticosteroid

81. Patients taking high doses of prednisone for an extended period of time are at risk of developing which of the following conditions?

a. Multiple sclerosis
b. Cushing's syndrome
c. Systemic lupus erythematosus
d. Addison's disease

Pregabalin

82. Which of the following is the brand name for pregabalin?

a. Lyrica
b. BromSite
c. Provigil
d. Cerebyx

83. Pregabalin belongs to which of the following pharmacologic classes?

a. Antianginal agent
b. Mast cell stabilizer
c. Anticonvulsant
d. Anaphylaxis agent

84. Pregabalin is indicated for the treatment of which of the following conditions?

a. Fibromyalgia
b. Alzheimer's disease
c. IBS
d. Insomnia

85. Pregabalin belongs to which of the following DEA Schedules?

a. Schedule II
b. Schedule III
c. Schedule IV
d. Schedule V

Prochlorperazine

86. Which of the following is a brand name for prochlorperazine?

a. Butrans
b. Compazine
c. Tapazole
d. Fexmid

87. Prochlorperazine belongs to which of the following pharmacologic classes?

a. Bronchodilator
b. Antineoplastic agent
c. Antiemetic
d. Antimigraine agent

88. Prochlorperazine is contraindicated in children < _____ years old.

a. 2
b. 8
c. 10
d. 16

Progesterone

89. Which of the following is a brand name for progesterone?

a. Phoslyra
b. Renova
c. Survanta
d. Prometrium

90. Progesterone capsules should be avoided in patients with an allergy to which of the following?

a. Soy
b. Peanuts
c. Shellfish
d. Eggs

Promethazine

91. Which of the following is a brand name for promethazine?

a. Phenergan
b. Moxeza
c. Relafen
d. Dolobid

92. Promethazine belongs to which of the following pharmacologic classes?

a. Macrolide antibiotic
b. H_1 antagonist
c. Factor Xa inhibitor
d. Tumor necrosis factor inhibitor

93. Promethazine is indicated for the treatment of which of the following conditions?

a. Osteoporosis
b. Schizophrenia
c. Glaucoma
d. Motion sickness

94. Promethazine is contraindicated in children less than 2 years old due to the risk of which of the following?

a. Reye's syndrome
b. Seizures
c. Respiratory depression
d. Skin reactions

Propafenone

95. Which of the following is the brand name for propafenone?

a. Rythmol SR
b. Diuril
c. Soltamox
d. Brisdelle

96. Propafenone belongs to which of the following pharmacologic classes?

a. Antidiabetic
b. Anticoagulant
c. GI stimulant
d. Antiarrhythmic agent

97. Propafenone is contraindicated in patients with which of the following conditions?

a. Osteoporosis
b. Heart failure
c. Anemia
d. Hypertension

Propranolol

98. Which of the following is a brand name for propranolol?

a. Dyrenium
b. Patanol
c. Inderal LA
d. Maxidex

99. Propranolol belongs to which of the following pharmacologic classes?

a. Beta-blocker
b. Anticholinergic
c. H_2 receptor antagonist
d. SNRI

100. Propranolol is indicated for the treatment of which of the following conditions?

a. Depression
b. Peptic ulcer disease
c. DVT
d. Hypertension

101. Propranolol should be used with caution in patients with which of the following conditions?

a. Asthma
b. Gout
c. Hepatitis
d. Epilepsy

Quetiapine

102. Which of the following is the brand name for quetiapine?

a. Focalin XR
b. Seroquel
c. Procrit
d. Zinecard

103. Quetiapine belongs to which of the following pharmacologic classes?

a. Diuretic
b. Hypnotic
c. Immunosuppressant
d. Antipsychotic

104. All but which of the following tests should be performed periodically in patients taking quetiapine?

a. Fasting blood glucose test
b. Eye exam
c. Pulmonary function test
d. Fasting lipid profile

Quinapril

105. Which of the following is the brand name for quinapril?

a. Accupril
b. Invokamet
c. Macrobid
d. Durezol

106. Quinapril belongs to which of the following pharmacologic classes?

a. Cholinergic agonist
b. NSAID
c. PDE-5 inhibitor
d. ACE inhibitor

107. Quinapril is available in which of the following dosage forms?

a. Transdermal patch
b. Oral tablet
c. Ophthalmic suspension
d. Oral solution

Raloxifene

108. Which of the following is the brand name for raloxifene?

a. Nucala
b. Robaxin
c. Evista
d. Dutoprol

109. Raloxifene belongs to which of the following pharmacologic classes?

a. SERM
b. Beta$_2$-agonist
c. DPP-4 inhibitor
d. ARB

110. Raloxifene is indicated for the treatment of which of the following conditions?

a. Hypothyroidism
b. Rheumatoid arthritis
c. Anxiety
d. Osteoporosis

111. Which of the following is the most appropriate dosing for raloxifene?

a. 60 mg once daily
b. 60 mg twice daily
c. 60 mg three times daily
d. 60 mg once weekly

Ramipril

112. Which of the following is the brand name for ramipril?

a. Elocon
b. Altace
c. Praluent
d. Salagen

113. Ramipril belongs to which of the following pharmacologic classes?

a. Sulfonylurea
b. COX-2 inhibitor
c. Dopamine antagonist
d. ACE inhibitor

114. Ramipril is indicated for the treatment of which of the following conditions?

a. Allergic rhinitis
b. Psoriasis
c. Hypertension
d. ADHD

Ranitidine

115. Which of the following is the brand name for ranitidine?

a. Zantac
b. Arthrotec
c. Trexall
d. Soolantra

116. Ranitidine belongs to which of the following pharmacologic classes?

a. Incretin mimetic
b. Bile acid sequestrant
c. Leukotriene receptor antagonist
d. H_2 receptor antagonist

117. Ranitidine is indicated for the treatment of which of the following conditions?

a. Insomnia
b. GERD
c. Anemia
d. BPH

Ranolazine

118. Which of the following is the brand name for ranolazine?

a. Diovan HCT
b. Sabril
c. Ranexa
d. Zohydro ER

119. Ranolazine belongs to which of the following pharmacologic classes?

a. Antianginal agent
b. ARB
c. Expectorant
d. Antineoplastic agent

120. The concomitant use of which of the following types of medications is contraindicated with ranolazine?

a. CYP2D6 inducers
b. Beta-blockers
c. CYP3A4 inhibitors
d. Nitrates

Rifaximin

121. Which of the following is the brand name for rifaximin?

a. Lotrisone
b. Varubi
c. Gengraf
d. Xifaxin

122. Rifaximin belongs to which of the following pharmacologic classes?

a. Estrogen receptor antagonist
b. Antibiotic
c. Antidiabetic
d. Antihyperlipidemic

123. Rifaximin is indicated for the treatment of which of the following conditions?

a. Traveler's diarrhea
b. Osteoarthritis
c. Duodenal ulcers
d. UTI

Risedronate

124. Which of the following is a brand name for risedronate?

a. Vandazole
b. Indocin
c. Repatha
d. Actonel

125. Risedronate belongs to which of the following pharmacologic classes?

a. Bisphosphonate
b. Calcium channel blocker
c. Biguanide
d. PPI

126. Risedronate is indicated for the treatment of which of the following conditions?

a. Migraines
b. Gout
c. Osteoporosis
d. Heart failure

127. Which of the following is the correct dose for risedronate that is administered monthly?

a. 5 mg
b. 35 mg
c. 75 mg
d. 150 mg

Risperidone

128. Which of the following is the brand name for risperidone?

a. Vraylar
b. Risperdal
c. Ibrance
d. Altavera

129. Risperidone belongs to which of the following pharmacologic classes?

a. Antipsychotic
b. Analgesic
c. Antidepressant
d. Antihistamine

130. Risperidone is indicated for the treatment of all but which of the following conditions?

a. Schizophrenia
b. Bipolar disorder
c. Obsessive compulsive disorder
d. Autistic disorder irritability

Rivaroxaban

131. Which of the following is the brand name for rivaroxaban?

a. Anoro Ellipta
b. Simponi
c. Lovaza
d. Xarelto

132. Rivaroxaban belongs to which of the following pharmacologic classes?

a. 5-alpha reductase inhibitor
b. Factor Xa inhibitor
c. PCSK9 inhibitor
d. Alpha$_2$-agonist

133. Rivaroxaban is indicated for the treatment of which of the following conditions?

a. DVT
b. Angina
c. Hyperlipidemia
d. Asthma

134. Rivaroxaban is available in all but which of the following oral tablet strengths?

a. 5 mg
b. 10 mg
c. 15 mg
d. 20 mg

Ropinirole

135. Which of the following is the brand name for ropinirole?

a. Duragesic
b. Sovaldi
c. Requip
d. Locoid

136. Ropinirole belongs to which of the following pharmacologic classes?

a. SGLT-2 inhibitor
b. SNRI
c. Cholinesterase inhibitor
d. Dopamine agonist

137. Ropinirole is indicated for the treatment of which of the following conditions?

a. Parkinson's disease
b. Depression
c. Hepatitis
d. Overactive bladder

138. Ropinirole may cause all but which of the following adverse effects?

a. Hallucinations
b. Insomnia
c. Nausea
d. Dizziness

Rosuvastatin

139. Which of the following is the brand name for rosuvastatin?

a. Crestor
b. Savaysa
c. Protonix
d. Lasix

140. Rosuvastatin belongs to which of the following pharmacologic classes?

a. Quinolone antibiotic
b. Thiazide diuretic
c. HMG-CoA reductase inhibitor
d. $5HT_3$ receptor antagonist

141. Rosuvastatin is indicated for the treatment of which of the following conditions?

a. Bipolar disorder
b. Hyperlipidemia
c. IBS
d. Cough

142. Which of the following tests should be performed when initiating therapy with rosuvastatin and periodically thereafter?

a. Liver function tests
b. Eye exam
c. Pulmonary function test
d. Fasting blood glucose

ANSWER KEY

1. A
A brand name for ofloxacin is Ocuflox.

2. D
Ofloxacin is classified as a fluoroquinolone antibiotic.

3. C
Ofloxacin is available as an ophthalmic solution, oral tablet, and otic solution. Ofloxacin is not available as a topical gel.

4. A
The brand name for olanzapine is Zyprexa.

5. B
Olanzapine is classified as an antipsychotic.

6. D
Among other parameters, patients taking olanzapine should have their blood pressure, weight, and lipids monitored. Monitoring liver enzymes is not necessary in patients taking olanzapine.

7. C
The brand name for olmesartan is Benicar.

8. A
Olmesartan is classified as an ARB.

9. B
Olmesartan may cause hyperkalemia.

10. D
The brand name for olmesartan-hydrochlorothiazide is Benicar HCT.

11. A
Olmesartan-hydrochlorothiazide is classified as an antihypertensive.

12. C
Olmesartan-hydrochlorothiazide is available as an oral tablet.

13. B
A brand name for olopatadine is Patanase.

14. D
Olopatadine is classified as an antihistamine.

15. C
The most appropriate dosing for olopatadine nasal spray is two sprays in each nostril twice daily.

16. A
A brand name for omega-3-acid ethyl esters is Lovaza.

17. B
Omega-3-acid ethyl esters are classified as an antihyperlipidemic.

18. D
Among other adverse effects, omega-3-acid ethyl acids may cause dysguesia, nausea, and diarrhea. Omega-3-acid ethyl esters are not associated with rhabdomyolysis.

19. A
Omega-3-acid ethyl esters should be used with caution when used concomitantly with medications that can increase bleeding risk, such as anticoagulants.

20. C
The brand name for omeprazole is Prilosec.

21. D
Omeprazole is classified as a PPI.

22. C
Omeprazole is available in 10 mg, 20 mg, and 40 mg oral capsules. Omeprazole is not available in 30 mg oral capsules.

23. A
Omeprazole may cause osteoporosis when used long term due to decreased calcium absorption.

24. B
A brand name for ondansetron is Zofran.

25. D
Ondansetron is classified as a 5-HT$_3$ receptor antagonist.

26. A
Ondansetron is indicated for the prevention of chemotherapy-induced, radiation-induced, and postoperative nausea and vomiting.

27. B
Ondansetron is available in 4 mg oral tablets, as well as 8 mg.

28. B
The brand name for oseltamivir is Tamiflu.

29. D
Oseltamivir is classified as an antiviral.

30. C

The correct dosing regimen for oseltamivir for the treatment of influenza in adults with normal renal function is 75 mg twice daily for 5 days.

31. B

Treatment with oseltamivir should be initiated within 48 hours of symptom onset.

32. D

A brand name for oxcarbazepine is Trileptal.

33. A

Oxcarbazepine is classified as an anticonvulsant.

34. C

Oxacarbazepine may cause hyponatremia.

35. B

A brand name for oxybutynin is Ditropan XL.

36. D

Oxybutynin is classified as a urinary antispasmodic.

37. A

Among other dosage forms, oxybutynin is available as a transdermal patch, oral tablet, and topical gel. Oxybutynin is not available as an oral capsule.

38. C

A brand name for oxycodone is OxyContin.

39. B

Oxycodone is classified as an opioid analgesic.

40. B

The levels of oxycodone can be increased by medications that inhibit CYP3A4.

41. C

The brand name for pantoprazole is Protonix.

42. B

Pantoprazole is classified a PPI.

43. D

Among other adverse effects, pantoprazole can increase the risk of *C. difficile* infection.

44. A

A brand name for paroxetine is Paxil.

45. C

Paroxetine is classified as an SSRI.

46. B
Among other indications, paroxetine is indicated for the treatment of major depressive disorder, social anxiety disorder, and panic disorder. Paroxetine is not indicated for the treatment of binge eating disorder.

47. D
A brand name for penicillin is Veetids.

48. C
Penicillin is classified as an antibiotic.

49. A
Penicillin V potassium should be taken on an empty stomach 1 hour before or 2 hours after meals to increase its absorption.

50. B
A brand name for phentermine is Adipex-P.

51. D
Phentermine is classified as an anorexiant.

52. A
Phentermine should be avoided in patients with hypertension because it can elevate blood pressure.

53. C
Phentermine belongs to DEA Schedule IV.

54. B
A brand name for phenytoin is Dilantin.

55. A
Phenytoin is classified as an anticonvulsant.

56. C
The therapeutic range for phenytoin is 10-20 mg/L.

57. D
Patients taking phenytoin long term may need supplementation with calcium, folic acid, and vitamin D. Phenytoin does not affect iron levels.

58. B
The brand name for pioglitazone is Actos.

59. A
Pioglitazone is classified as a thiazolidinedione.

60. C
Pioglitazone is indicated for the treatment of diabetes.

61. D
Pioglitazone should be used with caution in patients with congestive heart failure and is contraindicated in patients with NYHA class III or IV heart failure because it can cause edema.

62. B
A brand name for polyethylene glycol is Miralax.

63. A
Polyethylene glycol is classified as an osmotic laxative.

64. C
A brand name for potassium chloride is Klor-Con.

65. B
Potassium chloride should be taken with food, as well as a full glass of water or other liquid to minimize GI irritation.

66. D
The brand name for pramipexole is Mirapex.

67. A
Pramipexole is classified as a dopamine agonist.

68. D
Pramipexole is indicated for the treatment of Parkinson's disease, as well as restless leg syndrome.

69. C
Pramipexole is available as an oral tablet.

70. A
The brand name for prasugrel is Effient.

71. D
Prasugrel is classified as an antiplatelet agent.

72. A
Prasugrel is available in 10 mg oral tablets, as well as 5 mg.

73. C
The brand name for pravastatin is Pravachol.

74. B
Pravastatin is classified as an HMG-CoA reductase inhibitor.

75. D
Pravastatin is contraindicated in pregnancy due to the risk of birth defects.

76. A
A brand name for prednisolone is Millipred.

77. C
Prednisolone is classified as a corticosteroid.

78. B
Among other dosage forms, prednisolone is available as an oral solution, ophthalmic suspension, and oral tablet. Prednisolone is not available as a topical ointment.

79. C
A brand name for prednisone is Deltasone.

80. D
Prednisone is classified as a corticosteroid.

81. B
Patients taking high doses of prednisone for an extended period of time are at risk of developing Cushing's syndrome.

82. A
The brand name for pregabalin is Lyrica.

83. C
Pregabalin is classified as an anticonvulsant.

84. A
Among other indications, pregabalin is indicated for the treatment of fibromyalgia.

85. D
Pregabalin belongs to DEA Schedule V.

86. B
A brand name for prochlorperazine is Compazine.

87. C
Prochlorperazine is classified as an antiemetic.

88. A
Prochlorperazine is contraindicated in children < 2 years old.

89. D
A brand name for progesterone is Prometrium.

90. B
Progesterone capsules contain peanut oil and should be avoided in patients with a peanut allergy.

91. A
A brand name for promethazine is Phenergan.

92. B
Promethazine is classified as an H_1 antagonist.

93. D
In addition to other indications, promethazine is indicated for the treatment of motion sickness.

94. C
Promethazine is contraindicated in children less than 2 years old due to the risk of respiratory depression.

95. A
The brand name for propafenone is Rythmol SR.

96. D
Propafenone is classified as an antiarrhythmic agent.

97. B
Propafenone is contraindicated in patients with heart failure.

98. C
A brand name for propranolol is Inderal LA.

99. A
Propranolol is classified as a beta-blocker.

100. D
Propranolol is indicated for the treatment of hypertension.

101. A
Propranolol should be used with caution in patients with asthma due its non-selective beta-receptor blockade.

102. B
The brand name for quetiapine is Seroquel.

103. D
Quetiapine is classified as an antipsychotic.

104. C
In addition to other tests and monitoring parameters, patients taking quetiapine should have a fasting blood glucose test, eye exam, and fasting lipid profile performed periodically. Pulmonary function tests are not necessary in patients taking quetiapine.

105. A
The brand name for quinapril is Accupril.

106. D
Quinapril is classified as an ACE inhibitor.

107. B
Quinapril is available as an oral tablet.

108. C
The brand name for raloxifene is Evista.

109. A
Raloxifene is classified as a SERM.

110. D
In addition to other indications, raloxifene is indicated for the treatment of osteoporosis in postmenopausal women.

111. A
The most appropriate dosing for raloxifene is 60 mg once daily.

112. B
The brand name for ramipril is Altace.

113. D
Ramipril is classified as an ACE inhibitor.

114. C
Ramipril is indicated for the treatment of hypertension.

115. A
The brand name for ranitidine is Zantac.

116. D
Ranitidine is classified as an H_2 receptor antagonist.

117. B
Ranitidine is indicated for the treatment of GERD.

118. C
The brand name for ranolazine is Ranexa.

119. A
Ranolazine is classified as an antianginal agent.

120. C
The concomitant use of strong CYP3A4 inhibitors is contraindicated with ranolazine because it is a CYP3A4 substrate.

121. D
The brand name for rifaximin is Xifaxin.

122. B
Rifamixin is classified as an antibiotic.

123. A
Among other indications, rifaximin is indicated for the treatment of traveler's diarrhea.

124. D
A brand name for risedronate is Actonel.

125. A
Risedronate is classified as a bisphosphonate.

126. C
Among other indications, risedronate is indicated for the treatment of osteoporosis.

127. D
The correct dose for risedronate that is administered monthly is 150 mg.

128. B
The brand name for risperidone is Risperdal.

129. A
Risperidone is classified as an antipsychotic.

130. C
Risperidone is indicated for the treatment of schizophrenia, bipolar disorder, and irritability associated with autistic disorder. Risperidone is not indicated for the treatment of obsessive compulsive disorder.

131. D
The brand name for rivaroxaban is Xarelto.

132. B
Rivaroxaban is classified as a factor Xa inhibitor.

133. A
Among other indications, rivaroxaban is indicated for the treatment of DVT.

134. A
Rivaroxaban is available in 10 mg, 15 mg, and 20 mg oral tablets. Rivaroxaban is not available in 5 mg oral tablets.

135. C
The brand name for ropinirole is Requip.

136. D
Ropinirole is classified as a dopamine agonist.

137. A
Ropinirole is indicated for the treatment of Parkinson's disease, as well as restless leg syndrome.

138. B
Among other adverse effects, ropinirole may cause hallucinations, drowsiness, nausea, and dizziness.

139. A
The brand name for rosuvastatin is Crestor.

140. C
Rosuvastatin is classified as an HMG-CoA reductase inhibitor.

141. B
Rosuvastatin is indicated for the treatment of hyperlipidemia.

142. A
Liver function tests should be performed when initiating therapy with rosuvastatin and periodically thereafter.

DRUGS S – Z

QUESTIONS

<u>Saxagliptan</u>

1. Which of the following is the brand name for saxagliptan?

a. Necon
b. Prudoxin
c. Erygel
d. Onglyza

2. Saxagliptan belongs to which of the following pharmacologic classes?

a. Tricyclic antidepressant
b. DPP-4 inhibitor
c. Neurokinin-1 receptor antagonist
d. Alpha$_1$-agonist

3. Saxagliptan is indicated for the treatment of which of the following conditions?

a. Diabetes
b. COPD
c. Ulcerative colitis
d. Atopic dermatitis

4. Saxagliptan is available in which of the following dosage forms?

a. Subcutaneous solution
b. Oral inhalation
c. Transdermal patch
d. Oral tablet

<u>Sertraline</u>

5. Which of the following is the brand name for sertraline?

a. Rowasa
b. Lomotil
c. Atridox
d. Zoloft

6. Sertraline belongs to which of the following pharmacologic classes?

a. mTOR inhibitor
b. ACE inhibitor
c. SSRI
d. Renin inhibitor

7. Sertraline should not be used concomitantly with which of the following classes of medication?

a. MAO inhibitors
b. Sulfonylureas
c. Statins
d. Alpha-blockers

Sildenafil

8. Which of the following is a brand name for sildenafil?

a. Cosentyx
b. Viagra
c. Tricor
d. Inapsine

9. Sildenafil belongs to which of the following pharmacologic classes?

a. PDE-5 inhibitor
b. Vasopressin antagonist
c. Beta$_2$-agonist
d. Chloride channel activator

10. Sildenafil is contraindicated in patients taking which of the following classes of medication?

a. PPIs
b. Fibrates
c. Alpha-blockers
d. Nitrates

Simvastatin

11. Which of the following is a brand name for simvastatin?

a. Zocor
b. Dalvance
c. Prilosec
d. Lexiva

12. Simvastatin is indicated for the treatment of which of the following conditions?

a. Epilepsy
b. Hyperthyroidism
c. Hyperlipidemia
d. Arrhythmias

13. Simvastatin should be administered at which of the following times of day for maximal efficacy?

a. Before breakfast
b. After breakfast
c. Afternoon
d. Evening

Sitagliptan

14. Which of the following is the brand name for sitagliptan?

a. Oseni
b. Januvia
c. Zuplenz
d. Contrave

15. Sitagliptan is available in which of the following dosage forms?

a. Topical ointment
b. Oral capsule
c. Oral tablet
d. Intramuscular suspension

16. Which of the following is the maximum daily dose for sitagliptan?

a. 50 mg
b. 100 mg
c. 150 mg
d. 200 mg

Sodium fluoride

17. Which of the following is a brand name for sodium fluoride?

a. PreviDent
b. Duavee
c. Nyamc
d. Macugen

18. Sodium fluoride is used for the prevention of which of the following?

a. Gingivitis
b. Oral candidiasis
c. Canker sores
d. Dental caries

Solifenacin

19. Which of the following is the brand name for solifenacin?

a. Lodosyn
b. Vesicare
c. Omnipred
d. Epanova

20. Solifenacin belongs to which of the following pharmacologic classes?

a. Skeletal muscle relaxant
b. Carbonic anhydrase inhibitor
c. Anticholinergic
d. Benzodiazepine

21. Solifenacin is indicated for the treatment of which of the following conditions?

a. Overactive bladder
b. Glaucoma
c. Osteoporosis
d. Pulmonary embolism

22. Which of the following is the most appropriate dosing for solifenacin?

a. 10 mg once daily
b. 10 mg twice daily
c. 15 mg once daily
d. 15 mg twice daily

Spironolactone

23. Which of the following is a brand name for spironolactone?

a. Atacand
b. Natpara
c. Oxaydo
d. Aldactone

24. Spironolactone belongs to which of the following pharmacologic classes?

a. Fibrate
b. Potassium-sparing diuretic
c. $P2Y_{12}$ inhibitor
d. Estrogen receptor antagonist

25. Spironolactone is indicated for the treatment of which of the following conditions?

a. Heart failure
b. Multiple sclerosis
c. Glaucoma
d. Psoriasis

26. Spironolactone may cause which of the following adverse effects?

a. Respiratory depression
b. Gingival hyperplasia
c. Gynecomastia
d. Hypernatremia

Sucralfate

27. Which of the following is the brand name for sucralfate?

a. Abraxane
b. Tamiflu
c. Evicel
d. Carafate

28. Sucralfate belongs to which of the following pharmacologic classes?

a. Cytoprotective agent
b. Antianxiety agent
c. Laxative
d. Alzheimer's agent

29. Which of the following administration techniques applies to sucralfate?

a. Take with a meal.
b. Do not lie down for 60 minutes after taking.
c. Take on an empty stomach.
d. Antacids may be taken at the same time.

30. Sucralfate is available in which of the following oral tablet strengths?

a. 500 mg
b. 750 mg
c. 1,000 mg
d. 1,250 mg

Sulfamethoxazole-trimethoprim

31. Which of the following is a brand name for sulfamethoxazole-trimethoprim?

a. Pazeo
b. Bactrim
c. Adcetris
d. Uptravi

32. Sulfamethoxazole-trimethoprim belongs to which of the following pharmacologic classes?

a. Antiplatelet agent
b. Diuretic
c. Antiemetic
d. Antibiotic

33. Sulfamethoxazole-trimethoprim may cause all but which of the following adverse effects?

a. Tendon rupture
b. Crystalluria
c. Photosensitivity
d. Stevens-Johnson syndrome

34. Sulfamethoxazole-trimethoprim is available in all but which of the following dosage forms?

a. Intravenous solution
b. Ophthalmic suspension
c. Oral tablet
d. Oral suspension

Sulfasalazine

35. Which of the following is a brand name for sulfasalazine?

a. Azulfidine
b. Phenadoz
c. Baxdela
d. Cometriq

36. Sulfasalazine belongs to which of the following pharmacologic classes?

a. Aromatase inhibitor
b. Dopamine antagonist
c. Aminosalicylate
d. Protease inhibitor

37. Sulfasalazine is indicated for the treatment of which of the following conditions?

a. Osteoporosis
b. Diabetes
c. Breast cancer
d. Rheumatoid arthritis

38. Sulfasalazine impairs the absorption of which of the following vitamins?

a. Cyanocobalamin
b. Folate
c. Thiamine
d. Biotin

Sumatriptan

39. Which of the following is a brand name for sumatriptan?

a. Imitrex
b. Staxyn
c. Auvi-Q
d. Dacogen

40. Sumatriptan belongs to which of the following pharmacologic classes?

a. H_2 receptor antagonist
b. COX-2 inhibitor
c. Serotonin receptor agonist
d. Bile acid sequestrant

41. Sumatriptan is indicated for the treatment of which of the following conditions?

a. Anxiety
b. Migraines
c. Depression
d. ADHD

42. Sumatriptan is available in all but which of the following dosage forms?

a. Subcutaneous solution
b. Nasal spray
c. Oral tablet
d. Rectal suppository

Tacrolimus

43. Which of the following is a brand name for tacrolimus?

a. Mucomyst
b. Prograf
c. Hysingla ER
d. Lodine

44. Tacrolimus belongs to which of the following pharmacologic classes?

a. Immunosuppressant
b. Anticonvulsant
c. Bronchodilator
d. Anticoagulant

45. Tacrolimus is indicated for the prevention of which of the following conditions?

a. Peptic ulcer disease
b. Osteoporosis
c. Breast cancer
d. Organ transplant rejection

Tadalafil

46. Which of the following is a brand name for tadalafil?

a. Cialis
b. Makena
c. Procardia
d. Zurampic

47. Tadalafil belongs to which of the following pharmacologic classes?

a. Beta$_2$-agonist
b. Factor Xa inhibitor
c. PDE-5 inhibitor
d. Sulfonylurea

48. Tadalafil is indicated for the treatment of which of the following conditions?

a. Depression
b. Erectile dysfunction
c. Anemia
d. COPD

49. Tadalafil may cause all but which of the following adverse effects?

a. Hearing loss
b. Blurred vision
c. Headache
d. Hypertension

Tamoxifen

50. Which of the following is a brand name for tamoxifen?

a. Nolvadex
b. Genvoya
c. Rayos
d. Jevtana

51. Tamoxifen belongs to which of the following pharmacologic classes?

a. PPI
b. Incretin mimetic
c. SERM
d. Tricyclic antidepressant

52. Tamoxifen is indicated for the treatment of which of the following conditions?

a. Hyperlipidemia
b. Breast cancer
c. Gout
d. Alzheimer's disease

Tamsulosin

53. Which of the following is the brand name for tamsulosin?

a. Zinplava
b. Compro
c. Plavix
d. Flomax

54. Tamsulosin belongs to which of the following pharmacologic classes?

a. Alpha$_1$-blocker
b. Statin
c. SSRI
d. DPP-4 inhibitor

55. Tamsulosin is indicated for the treatment of which of the following conditions?

a. Hypertension
b. Osteoporosis
c. BPH
d. Heart failure

56. Which of the following administration techniques applies to tamsulosin?

a. Take 1 hour before breakfast.
b. Take with at least 8 oz. of water.
c. Take on an empty stomach before bedtime.
d. Take 30 minutes after the same meal each day.

Temazepam

57. Which of the following is the brand name for temazepam?

a. Ozurdex
b. Restoril
c. Glucovance
d. Prezista

58. Temazepam belongs to which of the following pharmacologic classes?

a. Benzodiazepine
b. Loop diuretic
c. SGLT-2 inhibitor
d. NSAID

59. Temazepam is indicated for the treatment of which of the following conditions?

a. Schizophrenia
b. Anxiety
c. Epilepsy
d. Insomnia

Terazosin

60. Which of the following is the brand name for terazosin?

a. Quartette
b. Naprosyn
c. Regimex
d. Hytrin

61. Terazosin belongs to which of the following pharmacologic classes?

a. CNS stimulant
b. Alpha$_1$-blocker
c. Skeletal muscle relaxant
d. ACE inhibitor

62. Terazosin is indicated for the treatment of which of the following conditions?

a. BPH
b. Menopausal symptoms
c. Migraines
d. Overactive bladder

63. Terazosin may cause which of the following adverse effects?

a. QT prolongation
b. Upper respiratory tract infection
c. First-dose syncope
d. Pancreatitis

Testosterone

64. Which of the following is a brand name for testosterone?

a. AndroGel
b. Naftin
c. Xifaxan
d. Epitol

65. Testosterone is available in all but which of the following dosage forms?

a. Transdermal patch
b. Intramuscular solution
c. Topical ointment
d. Oral tablet

66. Testosterone is contraindicated in men with which of the following conditions?

a. Glaucoma
b. Prostate cancer
c. BPH
d. Angina

Thyroid USP

67. Which of the following is a brand name for thyroid USP?

a. Synthroid
b. Unithroid
c. Armour Thyroid
d. Levothroid

68. Thyroid USP contains which of the following?

a. Synthetic T_3 and T_4
b. Synthetic T_3
c. Desiccated T_3 and T_4
d. Synthetic T_4

69. Thyroid USP can be used for the treatment of which of the following conditions?

a. Hashimoto's disease
b. Graves' disease
c. Addison's disease
d. Cushing's syndrome

Ticagrelor

70. Which of the following is the brand name for ticagrelor?

a. Trandate
b. Hiprex
c. Afeditab CR
d. Brilinta

71. Ticagrelor belongs to which of the following pharmacologic classes?

a. Antiplatelet agent
b. Antidiarrheal
c. Tocolytic agent
d. Antipsychotic

72. The effectiveness of ticagrelor is decreased with concomitant use of aspirin greater than _____ mg/day.

a. 81 mg
b. 100 mg
c. 325 mg
d. 500 mg

Timolol

73. Which of the following is a brand name for timolol?

a. Nexavar
b. Extina
c. Brevicon
d. Timoptic

74. Timolol belongs to which of the following pharmacologic classes?

a. Cholinesterase inhibitor
b. Prostaglandin analog
c. Beta-blocker
d. Dopamine agonist

75. Timolol is indicated for the treatment of which of the following conditions?

a. Glaucoma
b. Overactive bladder
c. IBS
d. Allergic rhinitis

Tiotropium

76. Which of the following is a brand name for tiotropium?

a. Zontivity
b. Spiriva
c. Oleptro
d. Niacor

77. Tiotropium belongs to which of the following pharmacologic classes?

a. Carbonic anhydrase inhibitor
b. Opioid analgesic
c. Potassium-sparing diuretic
d. Anticholinergic

78. Tiotropium is indicated for the treatment of which of the following conditions?

a. Gout
b. Motion sickness
c. COPD
d. Influenza

79. Which of the following administration techniques is correct for the capsule dosage form of tiotropium?

a. Inhalation must be sufficient to hear or feel the capsule vibrate.
b. Open the capsule before inserting in the inhalation device.
c. Inhale the medication rapidly.
d. Capsules may be stored in the inhalation device.

Tizanidine

80. Which of the following is the brand name for tizanidine?

a. Lexapro
b. Aristada
c. Zanaflex
d. Kristalose

81. Tizanidine belongs to which of the following pharmacologic classes?

a. Calcium channel blocker
b. Skeletal muscle relaxant
c. ARB
d. Sedative

82. Tizanidine is available in all but which of the following oral capsule strengths?

a. 2 mg
b. 4 mg
c. 6 mg
d. 8 mg

Tolterodine

83. Which of the following is the brand name for tolterodine?

a. Detrol
b. Incruse Ellipta
c. Maxitrol
d. Cozaar

84. Tolterodine belongs to which of the following pharmacologic classes?

a. Bone resorption inhibitor
b. Cephalosporin antibiotic
c. Anticholinergic
d. Antineoplastic agent

85. Tolterodine is indicated for the treatment of which of the following conditions?

a. Hypertension
b. Overactive bladder
c. Pulmonary embolism
d. Atrial fibrillation

86. Tolterodine may cause all but which of the following adverse effects?

a. Blurred vision
b. Insomnia
c. Constipation
d. Dry mouth

Topiramate

87. Which of the following is a brand name for topiramate?

a. Concerta
b. Keytruda
c. Westcort
d. Topamax

88. Topiramate belongs to which of the following pharmacologic classes?

a. Inotropic agent
b. Analgesic
c. Anticonvulsant
d. Antianxiety agent

89. Topiramate is indicated for the prevention of which of the following?

a. Migraines
b. Anemia
c. Gout
d. Osteoporosis

90. Topiramate may cause all but which of the following adverse effects?

a. Metabolic acidosis
b. Nephrolithiasis
c. Oligohydrosis
d. Weight gain

Torsemide

91. Which of the following is a brand name for torsemide?

a. Crinone
b. Demedex
c. ProAir HFA
d. Ventavis

92. Torsemide belongs to which of the following pharmacologic classes?

a. Loop diuretic
b. SNRI
c. Benzodiazepine
d. GI stimulant

93. Torsemide is indicated for the treatment of which of the following conditions?

a. Vertigo
b. Angina
c. Hypertension
d. Asthma

94. Patients taking high doses of torsemide should be monitored for which of the following adverse effects?

a. Cholelithiasis
b. Anemia
c. Vision loss
d. Ototoxicity

Tramadol

95. Which of the following is a brand name for tramadol?

a. Ultram
b. Concerta
c. Xartemis XR
d. Lumigan

96. Tramadol belongs to which of the following pharmacologic classes?

a. NSAID
b. Antithyroid agent
c. Opioid analgesic
d. Meglitinide

97. Tramadol should be avoided in patients with a history of which of the following?
a. ADHD
b. Seizures
c. GERD
d. Gout

Tramadol-acetaminophen

98. Which of the following is the brand name for tramadol-acetaminophen?

a. Xigduo XR
b. Atarax
c. Zioptan
d. Ultracet

99. Tramadol-acetaminophen is available in which of the following oral tablet strengths?

a. 37.5-300 mg
b. 37.5-325 mg
c. 50-300 mg
d. 75-325 mg

100. Tramadol-acetaminophen should be used with caution in combination with which of the following classes of medication?

a. SSRIs
b. Fenofibrates
c. NSAIDs
d. Sulfonylureas

Travoprost

101. Which of the following is a brand name for travoprost?

a. Gelnique
b. Travatan
c. Amitiza
d. Phenytek

102. Travoprost belongs to which of the following pharmacologic classes?

a. Alpha$_2$-agonist
b. Carbonic anhydrase inhibitor
c. Beta-blocker
d. Prostaglandin analog

103. Travoprost is indicated for the treatment of which of the following conditions?

a. Bacterial conjunctivitis
b. Dry eye
c. Glaucoma
d. Allergic conjunctivitis

104. Which of the following is the most appropriate dosing for travoprost?

a. 1 drop in affected eyes(s) once daily
b. 1 drop in affected eye(s) twice daily
c. 1 drop in affected eye(s) three times daily
d. 1 drop in affected eye(s) four times daily

Trazodone

105. Which of the following is a brand name for trazodone?

a. Noritate
b. Epaned
c. Zarah
d. Desyrel

106. Trazodone belongs to which of the following pharmacologic classes?

a. Hypnotic
b. Antidepressant
c. Anticoagulant
d. Antidiabetic

107. Trazodone may cause all but which of the following adverse effects?

a. Lymphedema
b. Priaprism
c. Orthostatic hypotension
d. Sedation

108. Trazodone is available in all but which of the following oral tablet strengths?

a. 50 mg
b. 100 mg
c. 150 mg
d. 200 mg

Triamcinolone

109. Which of the following is a brand name for triamcinolone?

a. Symbicort
b. Rytary
c. Kenalog
d. Invirase

110. Triamcinolone belongs to which of the following pharmacologic classes?

a. Corticosteroid
b. Antiviral
c. Antiemetic
d. Skeletal muscle relaxant

111. Topical triamcinolone can be used for the treatment of which of the following conditions?

a. Warts
b. Contact dermatitis
c. Acne
d. Cold sores

Triamterene-hydrochlorothiazide

112. Which of the following is a brand name for triamterene-hydrochlorothiazide?

a. Hyzaar
b. Centany
c. Tofranil
d. Maxzide

113. Triamterene-hydrochlorothiazide belongs to which of the following pharmacologic classes?

a. Prokinetic agent
b. Antihypertensive
c. Respiratory agent
d. Antidiarrheal

114. Triamterene-hydrochlorothiazide acts on which of the following part(s) of the nephron?

a. Collecting duct
b. Proximal tubule
c. Distal convoluted tubule and collecting duct
d. Loop of Henle and proximal tubule

115. Triamterene-hydrochlorothiazide has a black box warning regarding the risk of which of the following?

a. Hyperkalemia
b. Metabolic acidosis
c. Hyponatremia
d. Angioedema

Valacyclovir

116. Which of the following is the brand name for valacyclovir?

a. Celexa
b. Tecfidera
c. Zenatane
d. Valtrex

117. Valacyclovir belongs to which of the following pharmacologic classes?

a. Endocrine agent
b. Antiviral
c. Analgesic
d. Antifungal

118. Valacyclovir is available in which of the following dosage forms?

a. Topical cream
b. Intramuscular suspension
c. Oral tablet
d. Oral inhalation

Valsartan

119. Which of the following is a brand name for valsartan?

a. Diovan
b. Triesence
c. Xopenex
d. Klor-Con

120. Valsartan belongs to which of the following pharmacologic classes?

a. Benzodiazepine
b. COX-2 inhibitor
c. Calcium channel blocker
d. ARB

121. Valsartan may cause which of the following electrolyte abnormalities?

a. Hyponatremia
b. Hypercalcemia
c. Hyperkalemia
d. Hypomagnesemia

Valsartan-hydrochlorothiazide

122. Which of the following is the brand name for valsartan-hydrochlorothiazide?

a. Diovan HCT
b. Cardizem
c. Exforge HCT
d. Triklo

123. Valsartan-hydrochlorothiazide is indicated for the treatment of which of the following conditions?

a. Hypertension
b. Allergic rhinitis
c. BPH
d. Epilepsy

124. Valsartan-hydrochlorothiazide is available in which of the following dosage forms?

a. Nasal spray
b. Oral tablet
c. Transdermal patch
d. Topical ointment

Vardenafil

125. Which of the following is a brand name for vardenafil?

a. Pataday
b. Xarelto
c. Ecoza
d. Levitra

126. Vardenafil belongs to which of the following pharmacologic classes?

a. Thiazide diuretic
b. Alpha$_1$-blocker
c. PDE-5 inhibitor
d. Cholinesterase inhibitor

127. Vardenafil is indicated for the treatment of which of the following conditions?

a. Erectile dysfunction
b. Obesity
c. Depression
d. COPD

128. Patients using vardenafil should separate doses by at least _____ hours.

a. 8
b. 12
c. 24
d. 48

Varenicline

129. Which of the following is the brand name for varenicline?

a. Rebetol
b. Chantix
c. Apresoline
d. Ovocon

130. Varenicline belongs to which of the following pharmacologic classes?

a. Antidiabetic
b. Antiparkinson agent
c. CNS stimulant
d. Smoking cessation agent

131. Varenicline is available in which of the following dosage forms?

a. Oral tablet
b. Oral lozenge
c. Transdermal patch
d. Oral inhaler

Venlafaxine

132. Which of the following is the brand name for venlafaxine?

a. Otrexup
b. Adderall
c. Effexor
d. Glumetza

133. Venlafaxine belongs to which of the following pharmacologic classes?

a. $5HT_3$ receptor antagonist
b. SNRI
c. Beta$_1$-blocker
d. MAO inhibitor

134. Venlafaxine is indicated for the treatment of which of the following conditions?

a. Schizophrenia
b. Fibromyalgia
c. Insomnia
d. Major depressive disorder

Verapamil

135. Which of the following is a brand name for verapamil?

a. Calan
b. Prempro
c. Epogen
d. Advair Diskus

136. Verapamil belongs to which of the following pharmacologic classes?

a. Renin inhibitor
b. Calcium channel blocker
c. Dopamine agonist
d. ACE inhibitor

137. Verapamil may cause all but which of the following adverse effects?

a. Gingival hyperplasia
b. Edema
c. Constipation
d. Crystalluria

Vilazodone

138. Which of the following is the brand name for vilazodone?

a. Thalitone
b. Viibryd
c. Cambia
d. Alrex

139. Vilazodone belongs to which of the following pharmacologic classes?

a. Antidepressant
b. Opioid antagonist
c. Monoclonal antibody
d. Antipsychotic

140. Which of the following administration techniques applies to vilazodone?

a. Do not take at the same time as other medications or dietary supplements.
b. Take on an empty stomach.
c. Take with food.
d. Take with at least 8 oz. of water.

Warfarin

141. Which of the following is a brand name for warfarin?

a. Dificid
b. Ximino
c. Coumadin
d. Pexeva

142. Warfarin belongs to which of the following pharmacologic classes?

a. Gastric antisecretory
b. Anticoagulant
c. Sedative
d. Antiplatelet agent

143. Warfarin levels are affected by which of the following vitamins?

a. Vitamin C
b. Vitamin D
c. Vitamin E
d. Vitamin K

Ziprasidone

144. Which of the following is the brand name for ziprasidone?

a. Geodon
b. Cleocin
c. Viagra
d. Aldara

145. Ziprasidone belongs to which of the following pharmacologic classes?

a. Chemotherapeutic agent
b. Antipsychotic
c. Urinary antispasmodic
d. Antidepressant

146. Ziprasidone is contraindicated in patients with a history of which of the following?

a. Depression
b. Angioedema
c. Cholelithiasis
d. QT prolongation

Zolpidem

147. Which of the following is a brand name for zolpidem?

a. Canasa
b. Ambien
c. Vivlodex
d. Metaxall

148. Zolpidem belongs to which of the following pharmacologic classes?

a. Benzodiazepine
b. PPI
c. Hypnotic
d. Dopamine agonist

149. Zolpidem belongs to which of the following DEA Schedules?

a. Schedule II
b. Schedule III
c. Schedule IV
d. Schedule V

ANSWER KEY

1. D
The brand name for saxagliptan is Onglyza.

2. B
Saxagliptan is classified as a DPP-4 inhibitor.

3. A
Saxagliptan is indicated for the treatment of diabetes.

4. D
Saxagliptan is available as an oral tablet.

5. D
The brand name for sertraline is Zoloft.

6. C
Sertraline is classified as an SSRI.

7. A
Sertraline should not be used concomitantly with MAO inhibitors due to the risk of serotonin syndrome.

8. B
A brand name for sildenafil is Viagra.

9. A
Sildenafil is classified as a PDE-5 inhibitor.

10. D
Sildenafil is contraindicated in patients taking nitrates due to hypotension.

11. A
A brand name for simvastatin is Zocor.

12. C
Simvastatin is indicated for the treatment of hyperlipidemia.

13. D
Simvastatin should be administered in the evening for maximal efficacy because the rate of cholesterol synthesis in the liver peaks at nighttime.

14. B
The brand name for sitagliptan is Januvia.

15. C
Sitagliptan is available as an oral tablet.

16. B
The maximum daily dose for sitagliptan is 100 mg.

17. A
A brand name for sodium fluoride is PreviDent.

18. D
Sodium fluoride is used for the prevention of dental caries.

19. B
The brand name for solifenacin is Vesicare.

20. C
Solifenacin is classified as an anticholinergic.

21. A
Solifenacin is indicated for the treatment of overactive bladder.

22. A
Of the choices provided, the most appropriate dosing for solifenacin is 10 mg once daily.

23. D
A brand name for spironolactone is Aldactone.

24. B
Spironolactone is classified as a potassium-sparing diuretic.

25. A
Spironolactone is indicated for the treatment of heart failure.

26. C
Among other adverse effects, spironolactone may cause gynecomastia.

27. D
The brand name for sucralfate is Carafate.

28. A
Sucralfate is classified as a cytoprotective agent.

29. C
Sucralfate should be taken on an empty stomach. Antacids should be avoided 30 minutes before or after taking sucralfate.

30. C
Sucralfate is available in 1,000 mg oral tablets.

31. B
A brand name for sulfamethoxazole-trimethoprim is Bactrim.

32. D
Sulfamethoxazole-trimethoprim is classified as an antibiotic.

33. A
In addition to other adverse effects, sulfamethoxazole-trimethoprim may cause crystalluria, photosensitivity, and Stevens-Johnson syndrome. Sulfamethoxazole-trimethoprim is not associated with tendon rupture.

34. B
Sulfamethoxazole-trimethoprim is available as an intravenous solution, oral tablet, and oral suspension. Sulfamethoxazole-trimethoprim is not available as an ophthalmic suspension.

35. A
A brand name for sulfasalazine is Azulfidine.

36. C
Sulfasalazine is classified as an aminosalicylate.

37. D
Among other conditions, sulfasalazine is indicated for the treatment of rheumatoid arthritis.

38. B
Sulfasalazine impairs the absorption of folate.

39. A
A brand name for sumatriptan is Imitrex.

40. C
Sumatriptan is classified as a serotonin receptor agonist.

41. B
Sumatriptan is indicated for the treatment of migraines.

42. D
Among other dosage forms, sumatriptan is available as a subcutaneous solution, nasal spray, and oral tablet. Sumatriptan is not available as a rectal suppository.

43. B
A brand name for tacrolimus is Prograf.

44. A
Tacrolimus is classified as an immunosuppressant.

45. D
Tacrolimus is indicated for the prevention of organ transplant rejection.

46. A
A brand name for tadalafil is Cialis.

47. C
Tadalafil is classified as a PDE-5 inhibitor.

48. B
Tadalafil is indicated for the treatment of erectile dysfunction.

49. D
Among other adverse effects, tadalafil may cause hearing loss, blurred vision, headache, and orthostatic hypotension.

50. A
A brand name for tamoxifen is Nolvadex.

51. C
Tamoxifen is classified as a SERM.

52. B
Tamoxifen is indicated for the treatment of breast cancer.

53. D
The brand name for tamsulosin is Flomax.

54. A
Tamsulosin is classified as an alpha$_1$-blocker.

55. C
Tamsulosin is indicated for the treatment of BPH.

56. D
Tamsulosin should be taken 30 minutes after the same meal each day.

57. B
The brand name for temazepam is Restoril.

58. A
Temazepam is classified as a benzodiazepine.

59. D
Temazepam is indicated for the treatment of insomnia.

60. D
The brand name for terazosin is Hytrin.

61. B
Terazosin is classified as an alpha$_1$-blocker.

62. A
Terazosin is indicated for the treatment of BPH.

63. C
Among other adverse effects, terazosin may cause first-dose syncope.

64. A
A brand name for testosterone is AndroGel.

65. D
Among other dosage forms, testosterone is available as a transdermal patch, intramuscular solution, and topical ointment. Testosterone is not available as an oral tablet.

66. B
In addition to other contraindications, testosterone is contraindicated in men with prostate cancer.

67. C
A brand name for thyroid USP is Armour Thyroid.

68. C
Thyroid USP contains desiccated T_3 and T_4.

69. A
Thyroid USP can be used for the treatment of Hashimoto's disease, which can cause hypothyroidism.

70. D
The brand name for ticagrelor is Brilinta.

71. A
Ticagrelor is classified as an antiplatelet agent.

72. B
The effectiveness of ticagrelor is decreased with concomitant use of aspirin greater than 100 mg/day.

73. D
A brand name for timolol is Timoptic.

74. C
Timolol is classified as a beta-blocker.

75. A
Timolol is indicated for the treatment of glaucoma.

76. B
A brand name for tiotropium is Spiriva.

77. D
Tiotropium is classified as an anticholinergic.

78. C
Tiotropium is indicated for the treatment of COPD.

79. A
When using the capsule dosage form of tiotropium, inhalation must be slow and sufficient enough to hear or feel the capsule vibrate. The capsules should not be opened before inserting in the inhalation device. Capsules must be stored in the sealed blister packs.

80. C
The brand name for tizanidine is Zanaflex.

81. B
Tizanidine is classified as a skeletal muscle relaxant.

82. D
Tizanidine is available in 2 mg, 4 mg, and 6 mg oral capsules. Tizanidine is not available in 8 mg oral capsules.

83. A
The brand name for tolterodine is Detrol.

84. C
Tolterodine is classified as an anticholinergic.

85. B
Tolterodine is indicated for the treatment of overactive bladder.

86. B
Among other adverse effects, tolterodine may cause blurred vision, drowsiness, constipation, and dry mouth.

87. D
A brand name for topiramate is Topamax.

88. C
Topiramate is classified as an anticonvulsant.

89. A
Topiramate is indicated for the prevention of migraines, and is also indicated for the treatment of epilepsy.

90. D
In addition to other adverse effects, topiramate may cause metabolic acidosis, nephrolithiasis, oligohydrosis, and weight loss.

91. B
A brand name for torsemide is Demedex.

92. A
Torsemide is classified as a loop diuretic.

93. C
Torsemide is indicated for the treatment of hypertension, as well as edema associated with heart failure and hepatic or renal disease.

94. D
In addition to other monitoring parameters, patients receiving high doses of torsemide should be monitored for ototoxicity.

95. A
A brand name for tramadol is Ultram.

96. C
Tramadol is classified as an opioid analgesic.

97. B
Tramadol is associated with an increased risk of seizures and should be avoided in patients with a history of seizures.

98. D
The brand name for tramadol-acetaminophen is Ultracet.

99. B
Tramadol-acetaminophen is available in 37.5-325 mg oral tablets.

100. A
Tramadol-acetaminophen should be used with caution in combination with serotonergic medications, such as SSRIs, due to the risk of serotonin syndrome.

101. B
A brand name for travoprost is Travatan.

102. D
Travoprost is classified as a prostaglandin analog.

103. C
Travoprost is indicated for the treatment of glaucoma.

104. A
The most appropriate dosing for travoprost is 1 drop in affected eyes(s) once daily. Using travoprost more than once daily may decrease its effectiveness.

105. D
A brand name for trazodone is Desyrel.

106. B
Trazodone is classified as an antidepressant.

107. A
Among other adverse effects, trazodone may cause priaprism, orthostatic hypotension, and sedation. Trazodone is not associated with lymphedema.

108. D
Trazodone is available in 50 mg, 100 mg, and 150 mg oral tablets, as well as 300 mg. Trazodone is not available in 200 mg oral tablets.

109. C
A brand name for triamcinolone is Kenalog.

110. A
Triamcinolone is classified as a corticosteroid.

111. B
Topical triamcinolone can be used for the treatment of contact dermatitis.

112. D
A brand name for triamterene-hydrochlorothiazide is Maxzide.

113. B
Triamterene-hydrochlorothiazide is classified as an antihypertensive.

114. C
Triamterene-hydrochlorothiazide acts on the distal convoluted tubule and collecting duct.

115. A
Triamterene-hydrochlorothiazide has a black box warning regarding the risk of hyperkalemia.

116. D
The brand name for valacyclovir is Valtrex.

117. B
Valacyclovir is classified as an antiviral.

118. C
Valacyclovir is available as an oral tablet.

119. A
A brand name for valsartan is Diovan.

120. D
Valsartan is classified as an ARB.

121. C
Valsartan may cause hyperkalemia.

122. A
The brand name for valsartan-hydrochlorothiazide is Diovan HCT.

123. A
Valsartan-hydrochlorothiazide is indicated for the treatment of hypertension.

124. B
Valsartan-hydrochlorothiazide is available as an oral tablet.

125. D
A brand name for vardenafil is Levitra.

126. C
Vardenafil is classified as a PDE-5 inhibitor.

127. A
Vardenafil is indicated for the treatment of erectile dysfunction.

128. C
Patients using vardenafil should separate doses by at least 24 hours.

129. B
The brand name for varenicline is Chantix.

130. D
Varenicline is classified as a smoking cessation agent.

131. A
Varenicline is available as an oral tablet.

132. C
The brand name for venlafaxine is Effexor.

133. B
Venlafaxine is classified as an SNRI.

134. D
Among other indications, venlafaxine is indicated for the treatment of major depressive disorder.

135. A
A brand name for verapamil is Calan.

136. B
Verapamil is classified as a calcium channel blocker.

137. D
In addition to other adverse effects, verapamil may cause gingival hyperplasia, edema, and constipation. Verapamil is not associated with crystalluria.

138. B
The brand name for vilazodone is Viibryd.

139. A
Vilazodone is classified as an antidepressant.

140. C
Vilazodone should be taken with food to increase its absorption.

141. C
A brand name for warfarin is Coumadin.

142. B
Warfarin is classified as an anticoagulant.

143. D
Warfarin levels are affected by vitamin K.

144. A
The brand name for ziprasidone is Geodon.

145. B
Ziprasidone is classified as an antipsychotic.

146. D
Among other contraindications, ziprasidone is contraindicated in patients with a history of QT prolongation.

147. B
A brand name for zolpidem is Ambien.

148. C
Zolpidem is classified as a hypnotic.

149. C
Zolpidem belongs to DEA Schedule IV.

ABOUT THE AUTHOR

Renee Bonsell is a staff pharmacist at an independent pharmacy in Columbus, Ohio. She earned her Doctor of Pharmacy degree from The Ohio State University in 2012, where she graduated summa cum laude. Renee is the author of the books "Pharmacy Technician Certification Exam Practice Question Workbook," "NAPLEX Practice Question Workbook," and "Top 300 Drugs Practice Question Workbook," and she currently holds a Certification in Delivering Medication Therapy Management Services, a Pharmacy-Based Immunization Certification, and a Basic Life Support Certification. In addition, Renee is a member of the Ohio Pharmacists Association and the American Pharmacists Association.

INDEX

Index

Made in the USA
Lexington, KY
01 April 2019